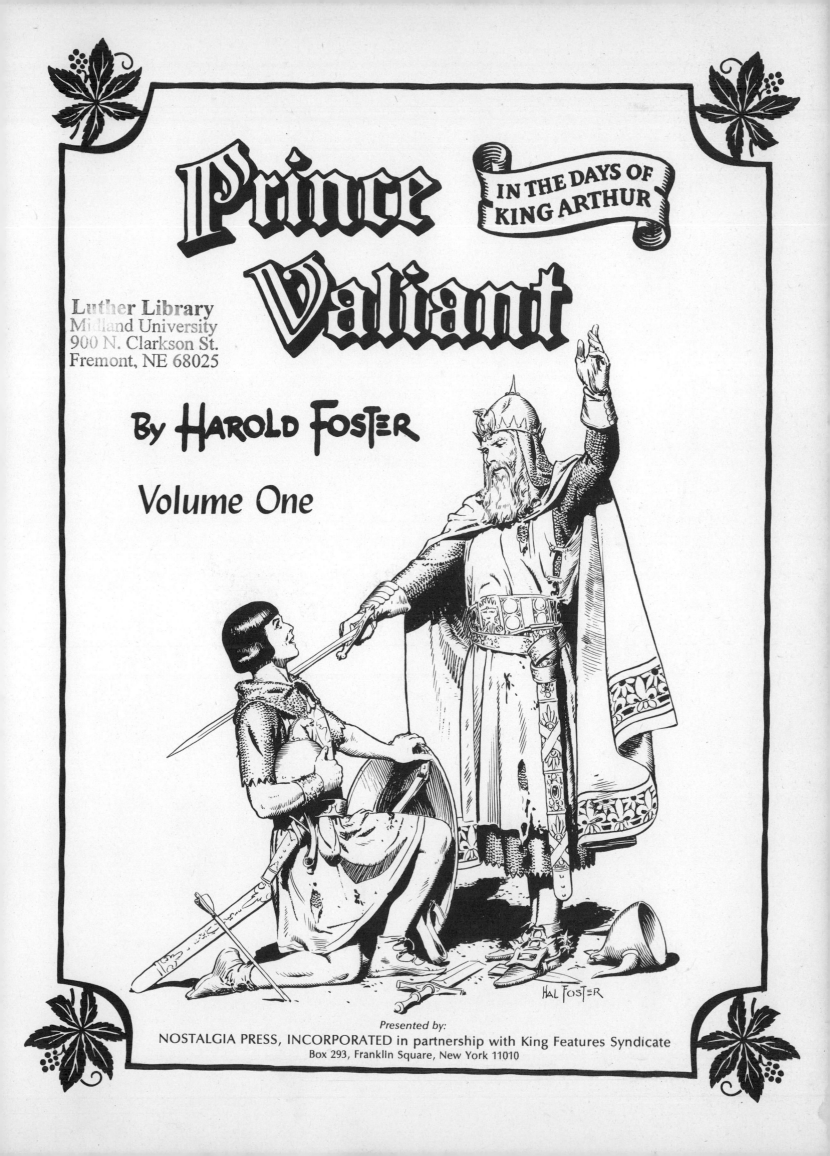

Prince Valiant

IN THE DAYS OF KING ARTHUR

By Harold Foster

Volume One

Presented by:
NOSTALGIA PRESS, INCORPORATED in partnership with King Features Syndicate
Box 293, Franklin Square, New York 11010

Contents

The Prophesy
February 13, 1937 to October 23, 1937

The Ogre
October 30, 1937 to February 19, 1938

The Fairy Morgana
February 26, 1938 to May 7, 1938

Prince Arn
May 15, 1938 to July 24, 1938

In the Service of King Arthur
July 31, 1938 to March 26, 1939

Knight Errant
April 2, 1939 to October 1, 1939

The Grand Victory
October 8, 1939 to January 14, 1940

Copyright 1974, King Features Syndicate and Nostalgia Press, Inc.
Library of Congress Catalog Number: 74-813-68

An Introduction

King Features and Nostalgia Press are proud to present **PRINCE VALIANT** in book form. This adventure strip, long recognized as one of the greatest works in the history of comic art, richly deserves to be part of the **Golden Age of the Comics** series.

Indeed, Hal Foster's **PRINCE VALIANT** has been acclaimed by millions of readers, among them the late Duke of Windsor, who called **PRINCE VALIANT** the "greatest contribution to English literature in the past hundred years." It is high praise for a man who never finished grammar school.

Harold Rudolph Foster was born into a seafaring family on August 16, 1892 in Halifax, Nova Scotia. By the time he was 10, young Hal was sailing a 30-foot sloop solo off the Canadian coast.

When his father's business failed in 1906, the family moved to Winnipeg, Manitoba, where Hal picked up his father's love of the outdoor life. In his 14th year, Hal spent a winter trapping for furs. That was also the year he learned to box—well enough to fight as a professional. Sandwiched in between these pursuits young Foster worked as a newsboy.

At 18, Hal entered the business world to help support his family only to discover it interfered with his hunting. Upon returning from one-too-many-extended-trips his employer boiled, "You seem to think duck hunting is more important than business!" Answered Hal: "Isn't it?" In minutes he was among the unemployed.

Just when Hal Foster learned to draw isn't clear but as he explained, "You learn to quick-sketch outdoors in Winnipeg because it's 20-30 below zero!" What talent he had was enough to secure a job with a mail order house as staff artist. It was a job he kept until Canada's pre-war depression in 1913 forced him into free-lancing.

In 1915 Hal met pretty blonde Helen Wells at a dance. They were married the same year and Foster says, "She is my secretary, housewife, treasurer, business manager and companion!"

To find work, the Fosters went to Ontario and Manitoba as hunter guides. By 1917 they added gold prospecting to their interests and in the Lake Rice region found "a million dollar claim." They worked the mine for nearly three years before the claim was jumped and the mine passed out of their control. Again Hal turned to art.

Neither the mail order job nor his free-lance experience was enough, he felt, to make it big in the art field. He now had two sons and a wife relying on his skill. This time Hal was determined to learn his craft well. He hauled out the bike and peddled his way 1,000 miles to Chicago where he studied at the Art Institute, Academy of Fine Arts and the National Academy. The Fosters became naturalized Americans and settled down to pursue an art career. "I was no darn good at a lot of things but I was always good at drawing," Foster said. "When I got some formal instruction everything came together."

It was slow at first but Foster's talent grew. He was accepting commissions for such clients as **Popular Mechanics** magazine when he was asked to illustrate a new popular novel for newspaper readers. The story was **Tarzan of the Apes** by Edgar Rice Burroughs and Foster was to illustrate a 10-week sequence to test reader reaction.

Tarzan was unique among the other strips of the day. The five-panel format was without balloons for dialogue and its text, which ran about 100 words per panel, was inserted out of the way of the artwork. The feature was a success but Foster had returned to his advertising accounts.

Two years later in 1931, when the daily and Sunday chores became too much work for the syndicate artist, Rex Maxon, Foster was again recruited to do the Sunday pages. For nearly six years Foster worked on the Sunday color Tarzan. He polished his illustrator's style and took the adventure strip to heights beyond the conventional Sunday Funnies. By 1936 he had outgrown the material. He needed a larger theme; a broader canvas.

On February 13, 1937, Hal Foster's **PRINCE VALIANT** arrived on the color pages of the New York Journal, to begin an epic trek through history. It also took the Fosters across Europe.

Wherever **PRINCE VALIANT** travels, the Fosters have been there first and authenticated the deeds of the Prince of Thule with some thorough research. The costumes, the weaponry and the geography are drawn from the original. On occasion Foster has admitted to bending history for the sake of the story, but his liberties are acceptable. **PRINCE VALIANT** is more than an adventure strip. It is an illustrated novel.

Others agree. The **Banshees** have awarded Foster the **Silver Lady** and the **National Cartoonists Society** have presented him with a **Reuben. PRINCE VALIANT** was made into a big-budget film by **20th Century Fox Pictures** and he has a following around the world.

King Features and Nostalgia Press herewith proudly present the first color portfolio of the adventures of **PRINCE VALIANT in the Days of King Arthur.**

The Prophesy

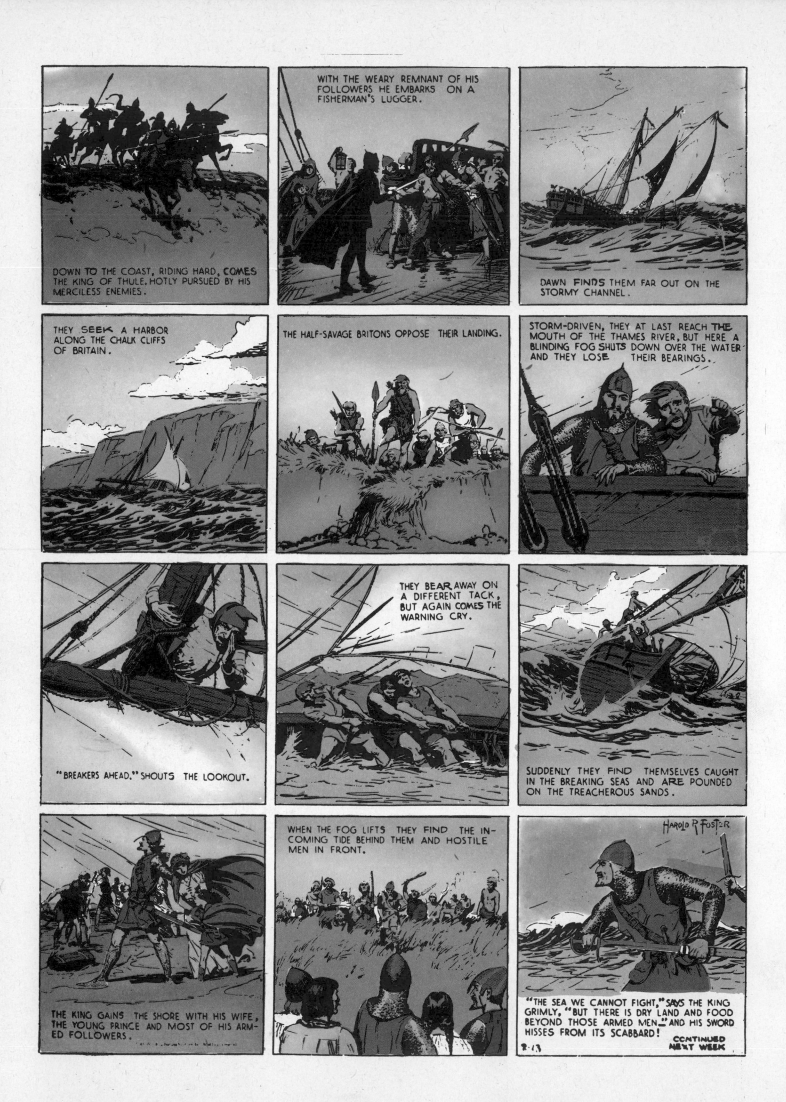

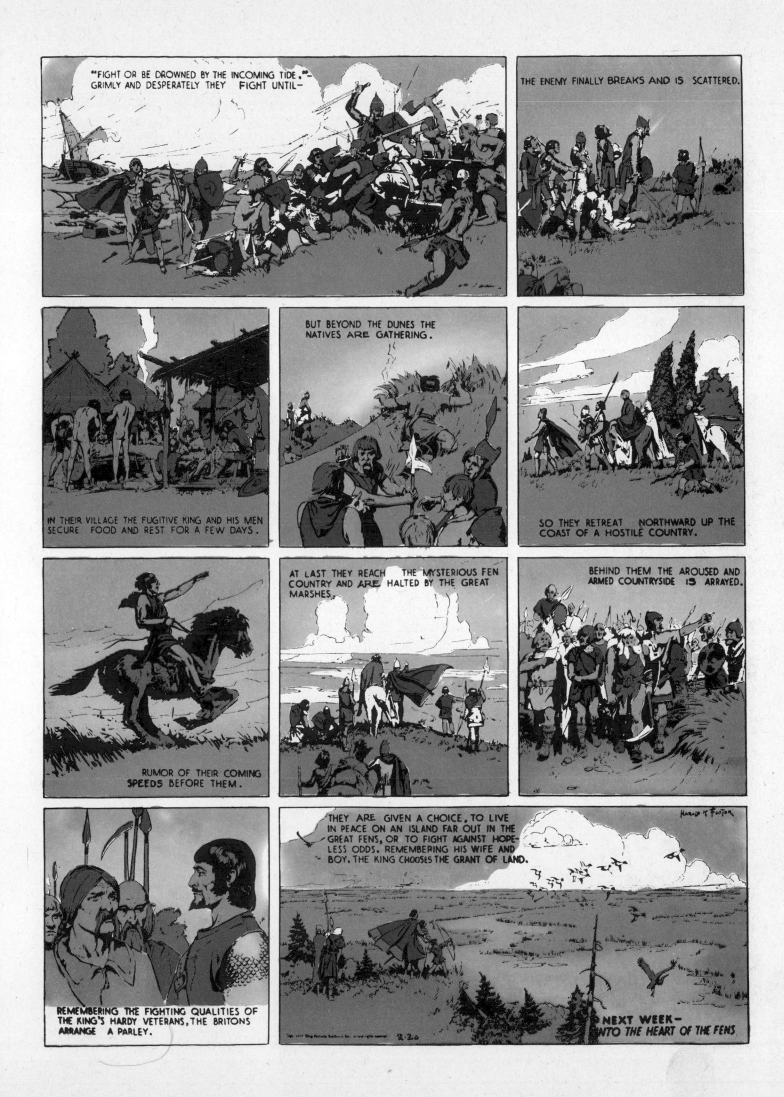

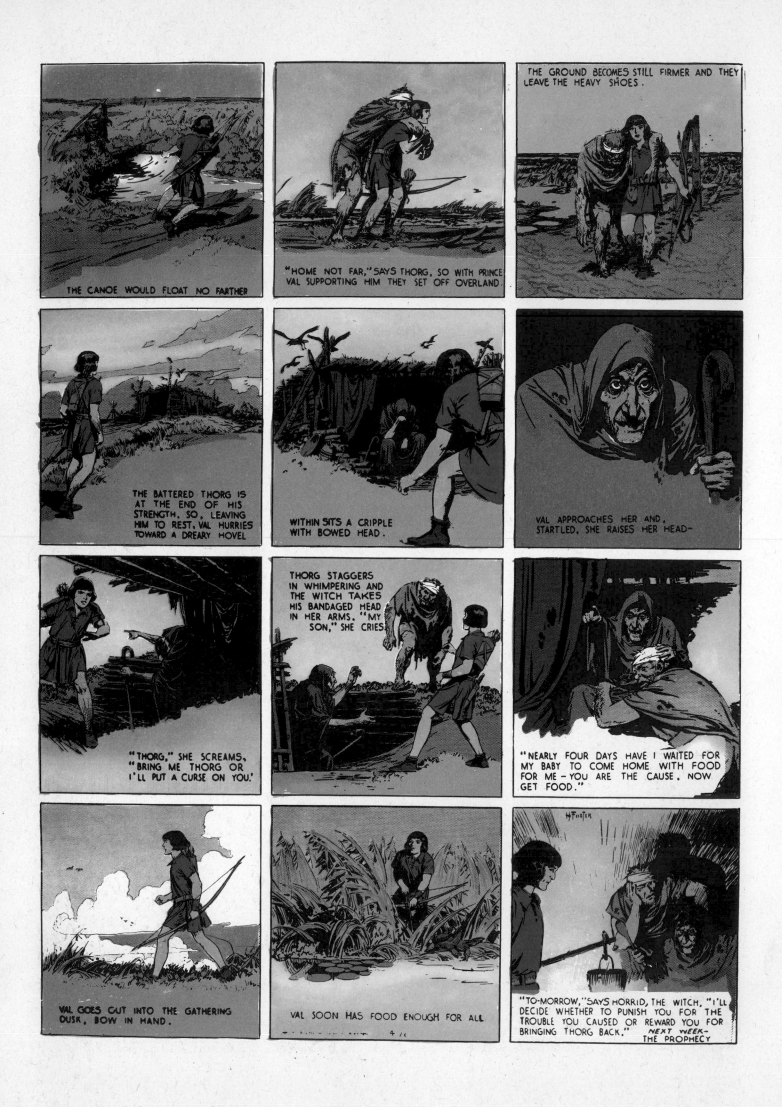

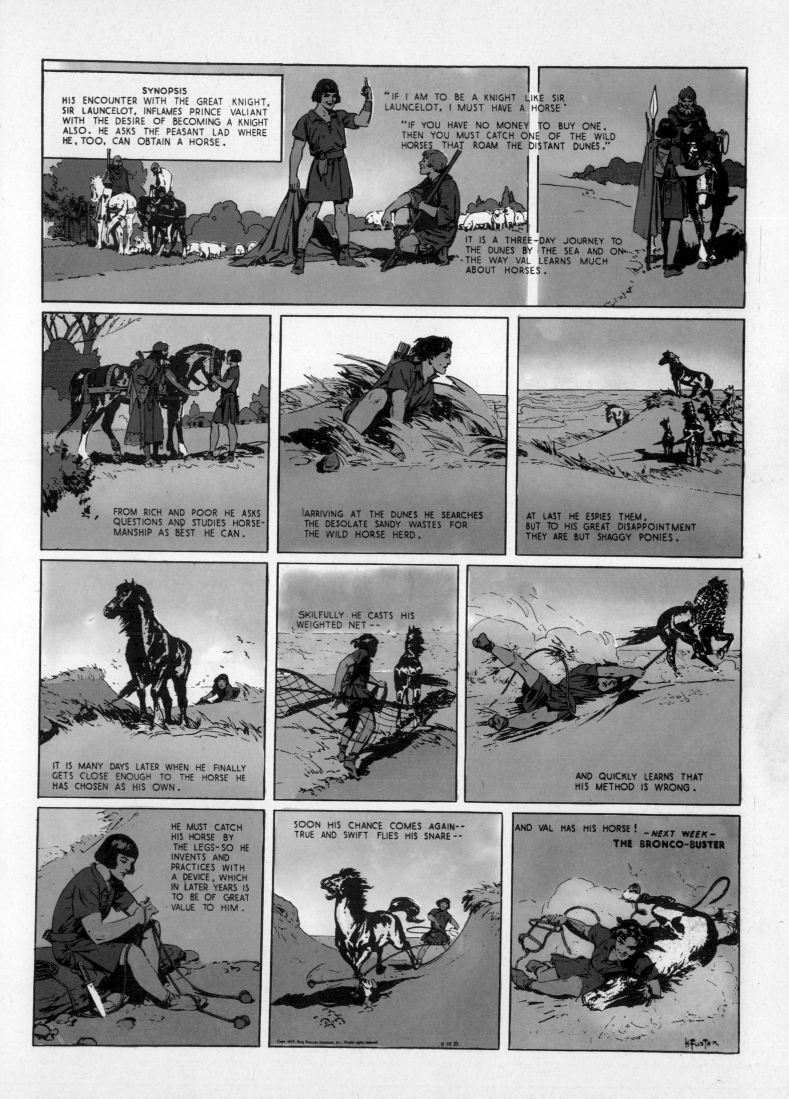

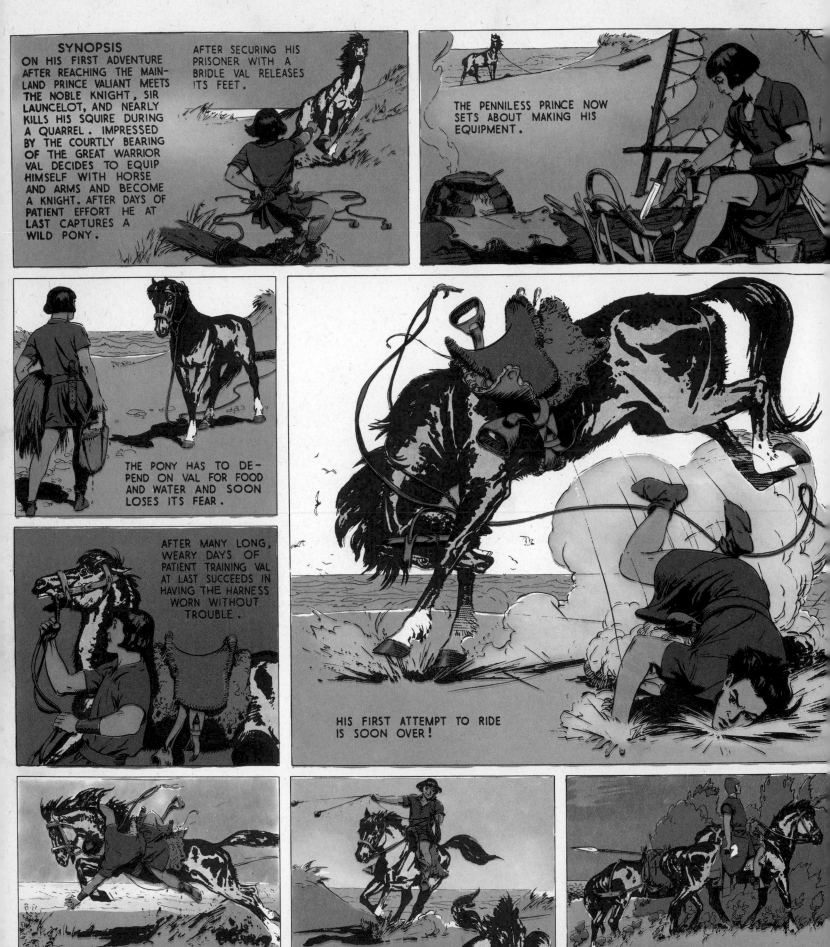

SYNOPSIS
ON HIS FIRST ADVENTURE AFTER REACHING THE MAINLAND PRINCE VALIANT MEETS THE NOBLE KNIGHT, SIR LAUNCELOT, AND NEARLY KILLS HIS SQUIRE DURING A QUARREL. IMPRESSED BY THE COURTLY BEARING OF THE GREAT WARRIOR VAL DECIDES TO EQUIP HIMSELF WITH HORSE AND ARMS AND BECOME A KNIGHT. AFTER DAYS OF PATIENT EFFORT HE AT LAST CAPTURES A WILD PONY.

AFTER SECURING HIS PRISONER WITH A BRIDLE VAL RELEASES ITS FEET.

THE PENNILESS PRINCE NOW SETS ABOUT MAKING HIS EQUIPMENT.

THE PONY HAS TO DEPEND ON VAL FOR FOOD AND WATER AND SOON LOSES ITS FEAR.

AFTER MANY LONG, WEARY DAYS OF PATIENT TRAINING VAL AT LAST SUCCEEDS IN HAVING THE HARNESS WORN WITHOUT TROUBLE.

HIS FIRST ATTEMPT TO RIDE IS SOON OVER!

BUT THE YOUNG PRINCE GRIMLY PERSEVERES AND SOON--

5-22-37

KNOWS THE SUPREME THRILL OF BEING 'A MAN ON HORSEBACK.'

AS SUMMER WANES A STRANGELY-ARMED KNIGHT-TO-BE LEAVES THE COAST AND RIDES OUT TO CONQUER THE WORLD.
NEXT WEEK: "THE HOME-MADE KNIGHT."

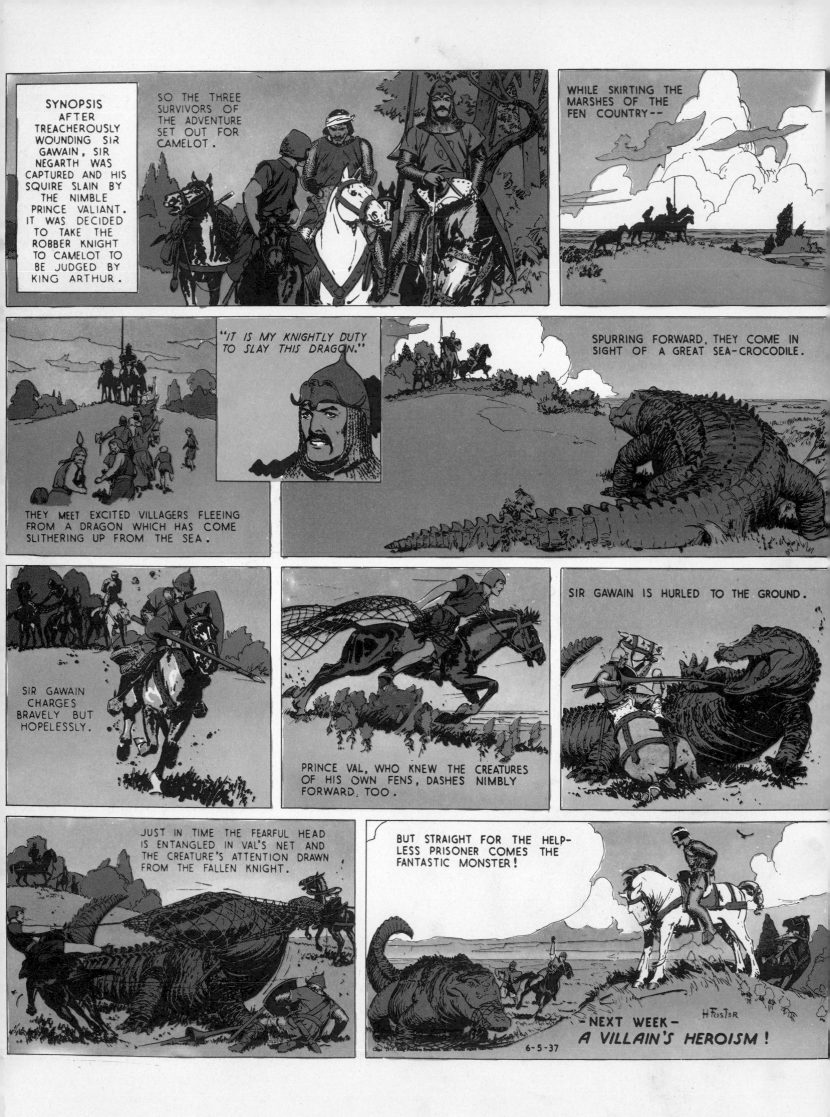

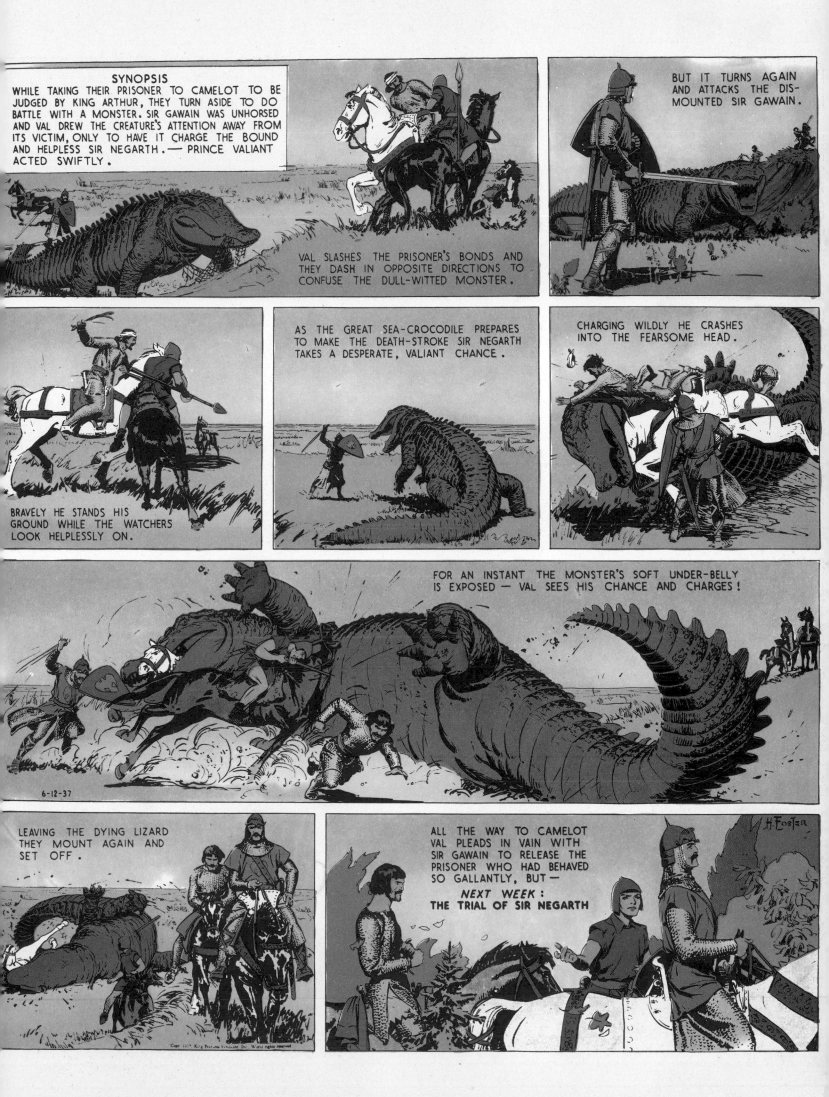

6-12-37

SYNOPSIS
WHILE TAKING THEIR PRISONER TO CAMELOT TO BE JUDGED BY KING ARTHUR, THEY TURN ASIDE TO DO BATTLE WITH A MONSTER. SIR GAWAIN WAS UNHORSED AND VAL DREW THE CREATURE'S ATTENTION AWAY FROM ITS VICTIM, ONLY TO HAVE IT CHARGE THE BOUND AND HELPLESS SIR NEGARTH. — PRINCE VALIANT ACTED SWIFTLY.

VAL SLASHES THE PRISONER'S BONDS AND THEY DASH IN OPPOSITE DIRECTIONS TO CONFUSE THE DULL-WITTED MONSTER.

BUT IT TURNS AGAIN AND ATTACKS THE DISMOUNTED SIR GAWAIN.

BRAVELY HE STANDS HIS GROUND WHILE THE WATCHERS LOOK HELPLESSLY ON.

AS THE GREAT SEA-CROCODILE PREPARES TO MAKE THE DEATH-STROKE SIR NEGARTH TAKES A DESPERATE, VALIANT CHANCE.

CHARGING WILDLY HE CRASHES INTO THE FEARSOME HEAD.

FOR AN INSTANT THE MONSTER'S SOFT UNDER-BELLY IS EXPOSED — VAL SEES HIS CHANCE AND CHARGES!

LEAVING THE DYING LIZARD THEY MOUNT AGAIN AND SET OFF.

ALL THE WAY TO CAMELOT VAL PLEADS IN VAIN WITH SIR GAWAIN TO RELEASE THE PRISONER WHO HAD BEHAVED SO GALLANTLY, BUT —

NEXT WEEK:
THE TRIAL OF SIR NEGARTH

SYNOPSIS
WHILE TAKING THEIR PRISONER, THE ROBBER KNIGHT, SIR NEGARTH, TO CAMELOT TO BE JUDGED BY KING ARTHUR, PRINCE VALIANT AND SIR GAWAIN BATTLE A STRANGE MONSTER AND ARE SAVED BY THE HEROIC CONDUCT OF SIR NEGARTH.
VAL PLEADS IN VAIN FOR SIR NEGARTH'S FREEDOM.

AT DAWN THEY SEE CAMELOT, THE CITY OF MARVEL, RISING SPIRE UPON SPIRE INTO THE CLOUDS.

VAL GASPS WITH WONDER AS THEY ENTER THE MERLIN GATE.

WITHIN THE COURTYARD ARE GATHERED MANY GREAT KNIGHTS WHOSE DEEDS STILL LIVE IN SONG AND STORY.

DESPITE VAL'S PLEA THE GALLANT SIR NEGARTH IS LODGED IN A CELL TO AWAIT HIS JUDGMENT.

AT SUNSET HERALDS ANNOUNCE THE PRESENCE OF KING ARTHUR IN THE HALL OF JUSTICE AND SUMMON ALL TO ATTEND.

AMONG THE MEN-AT-ARMS AT THE REAR OF THE HALL PRINCE VALIANT SULLENLY AWAITS THE TRIAL HE WAS UNABLE TO PREVENT.

CONTINUED: THE TRIAL OF SIR NEGARTH

H. FOSTER   6-19-37

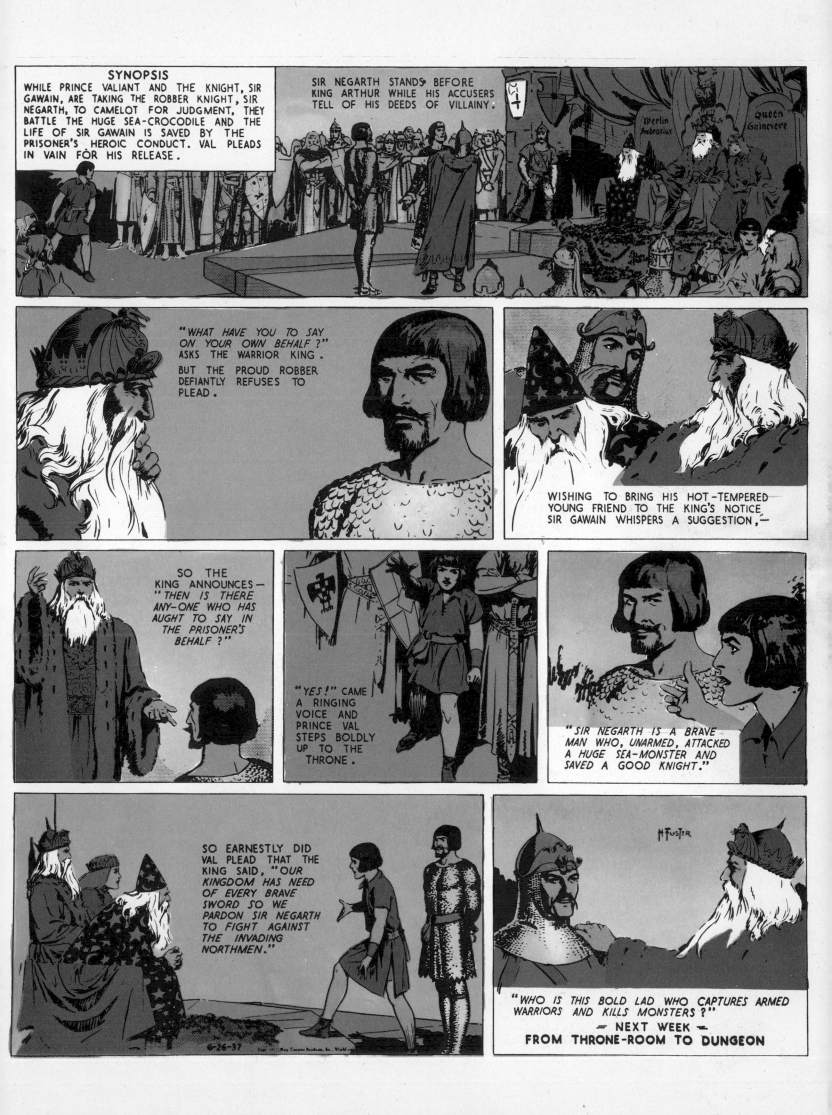

SIR GAWAIN FINDS HIS YOUNG FRIEND AT HIS EVERLASTING WARLIKE PRACTICING AND TELLS OF THE KING'S WISH.

SO PRINCE VALIANT IS PRESENTED TO KING ARTHUR AND QUEEN GUINEVERE — THIS ALSO HAD BEEN PROPHESIED BY THE WITCH!

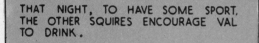

VAL TELLS OF HIS LIFE IN THE WILD FENS, HIS NOBLE BIRTH AND HIS DESIRE TO BECOME A KNIGHT. HE LEARNS THAT HE MUST FIRST WIN HIS SPURS BY DEEDS OF VALOR AND AGREES TO BECOME SIR GAWAIN'S SQUIRE.

CONTROLLING HIS FIERY PRIDE HE SETS ABOUT HIS DUTIES WITH A WILL.

THAT NIGHT, TO HAVE SOME SPORT, THE OTHER SQUIRES ENCOURAGE VAL TO DRINK.

THEN WITH FLATTERY, GET HIM TO TALK OF HIS HIGH AMBITIONS.

AT WHICH THEY LAUGH UPROARIOUSLY!

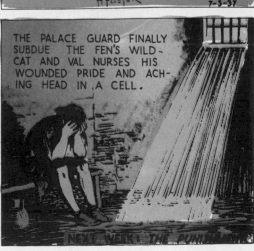

H FOSTER   7-3-37

VAL'S QUICK TEMPER FLAMES AND THE FIGHT THAT FOLLOWS IS A CLASSIC!

THE PALACE GUARD FINALLY SUBDUE THE FEN'S WILD-CAT AND VAL NURSES HIS WOUNDED PRIDE AND ACH-ING HEAD IN A CELL.

NEXT WEEK: THE PUNISHMENT

SIR OSMOND AND THE BARON BALDON PLAN CAREFULLY.

IN THE SPRING KING ARTHUR RETURNS VICTORIOUS !

AND SIR GAWAIN'S MIGHTY DEEDS IN BATTLE WON HIM THE KING'S FAVOR.

SO THE TWO CONSPIRATORS PICK HIM AS THE VICTIM OF THEIR RANSOM PLOT.

7-17-37

TO FURTHER THEIR PLAN THEY BEFRIEND VAL AND TELL HIM WONDROUS TALES OF THE DISTANT CASTLE OF EREIWOLD—

UNTIL VAL COULD TALK OF NOTHING ELSE BUT HIS DESIRE TO SEE THIS MOUNTAIN PALACE OF MARVEL. HIS ENTHUSIASM AROUSES SIR GAWAIN'S CURIOUSITY, TOO.
NEXT WEEK: *HOW THE PLOT WORKS*

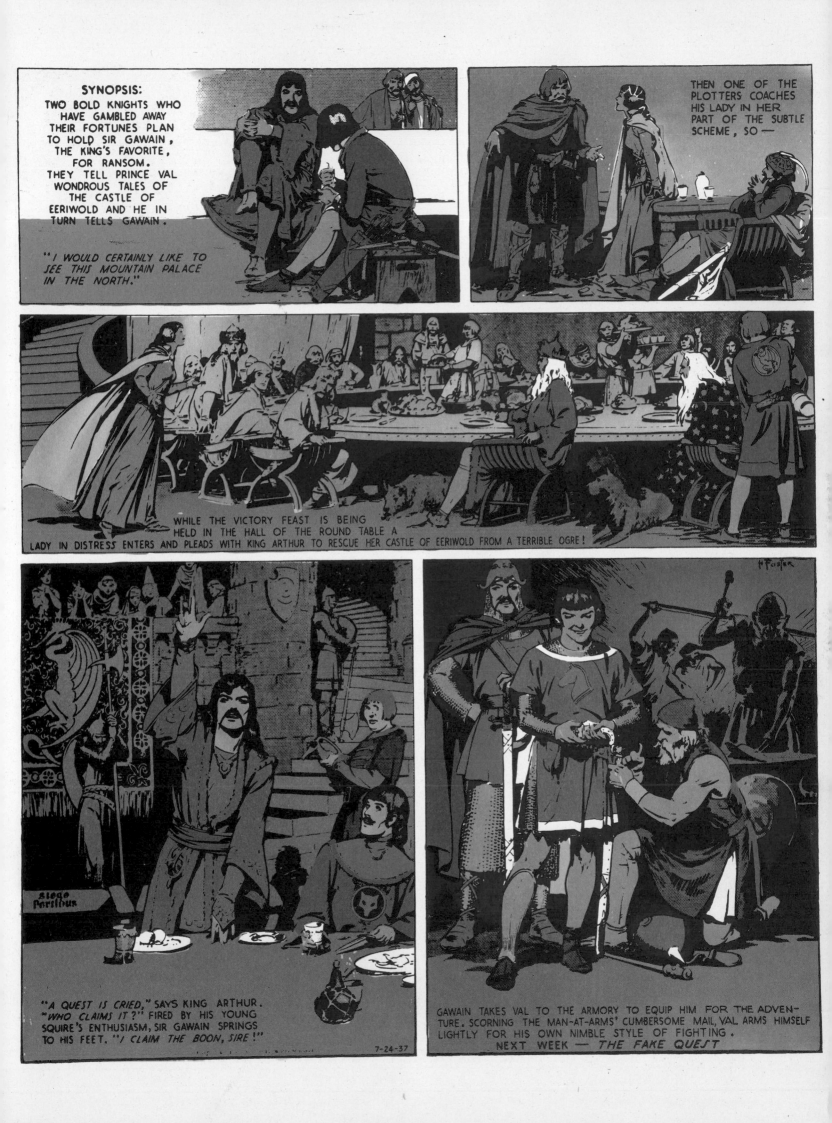

SYNOPSIS: PLANNING TO HOLD FOR RANSOM THE KING'S FAVORITE, BRAVE SIR GAWAIN, THE PLOTTERS CLEVERLY DECOY HIM INTO ACCEPTING A FALSE QUEST.

AT DAWN OF A STORMY APRIL DAY GAWAIN, VAL AND THE LADY MORVYN SET OUT UPON THE ADVENTURE.

AFTER MAKING SURE THEIR PROPOSED VICTIM IS WELL ON HIS WAY THE CONSPIRATORS, LIGHTLY ARMED, RACE AHEAD TO PREPARE THE TRAP.

BUT IN A FOREST GLADE THEY ENCOUNTER THREE KNIGHTS WHO CHALLENGE THEM TO FIGHT AS IS THE CUSTOM IN THESE ROUGH DAYS.

THINGS ARE GOING BADLY FOR THE TWO PLOTTERS WHEN GAWAIN AND VAL RIDE INTO THE GLADE.

SEEING THE UNEQUAL CONTEST, SIR GAWAIN CHARGES WITH DEADLY FORCE, UNHORSING ONE KNIGHT, WHILE PRINCE VAL ADDRESSES THE OTHER—

ONLY TO LEARN PAINFULLY THAT HE IS AS YET NO MATCH FOR AN EXPERIENCED, HEAVILY-ARMED KNIGHT !

BUT WHEN FORCE FAILS WIT WINS !

7-31-37

H Foster

AND VAL BATTERS HIS ADVERSARY INTO A MORE PEACEABLE FRAME OF MIND.
NEXT WEEK: THE FAKE QUEST, CONTINUED

SO SIR GAWAIN AND
PRINCE VAL UNKNOWINGLY
RESCUE THE TWO MEN
WHO ARE PLOTTING TO
BETRAY THEM.

THE THREE VANQUISHED KNIGHTS
ARE BOUND BY OATH TO SERVE
KING ARTHUR.

"WE WILL ESCORT THEM
SAFELY TO CAMELOT."

BUT ONCE OUT OF SIGHT THEY DESERT
THEIR TRUST AND SPEED AHEAD TO
COMPLETE THEIR EVIL DESIGN.

THE BRAVE GAWAIN AND NIMBLE VAL AGAIN
TAKE UP THE QUEST THAT IS TO RESTORE TO
THE LADY MORVYN HER CASTLE, EERIWOLD.

TO GIVE HER ACCOMPLICES TIME TO SET
WELL THEIR CLEVER TRAP, SHE FEIGNS
FATIGUE.

6-7-37

THEY SEEK SHELTER WITHIN A
PEASANT'S THATCHED COTTAGE.

THERE IS
SOMETHING ABOUT
THIS ADVENTURE
THAT PUZZLES
VAL —
HE RESOLVES
TO BE
WATCHFUL.

H FOSTER

NEXT WEEK: THE FAKE QUEST, CONTINUED

SYNOPSIS: THE QUESTING PARTY COMES TO THE CASTLE OF EERIWOLD. BUT IT IN NO WAY RESEMBLES THE CASTLE VAL HAS HEARD SO MUCH ABOUT. IN THE GATHERING DUSK LADY MORVYN GUIDES THEM TO A SECRET WAY BY WHICH THEY CAN APPROACH UNOBSERVED.

THEY ASCEND A NARROW, ROCKY PATH-- LADY MORVYN LAGS FAR BEHIND.

SILENTLY A CLINGING NET DROPS FROM THE GREAT TREES OVERHEAD AND THE FOREST AWAKES TO THE SHOUTS OF ARMED MEN!

AMID THE TUMULT PRINCE VAL WORKS SWIFTLY, SILENTLY.

AND THE KNAVE WHO FLINGS HIMSELF UPON VAL MIGHT BETTER HAVE GRASPED A DEADLY SERPENT.

NIMBLY VAL SPEEDS INTO THE DARKENING FOREST.

FIERCELY HIS CAPTURE OR DEATH IS ORDERED.

NEXT WEEK-- *THE DISGUISE*

8-24-37

SYNOPSIS — ESCAPING FROM THE TRAP THE RANSOM PLOTTERS HAD SET FOR SIR GAWAIN, VAL HIDES IN THE DANGEROUS WOODS WHILE THE SOUND OF PURSUIT GOES ON ALL AROUND HIM.

IN THE GATHERING DUSK THE SEARCH DRAWS CLOSE AND THE YOUNG PRINCE FORMS A DARING PLAN.

CUTTING A STOUT SAPLING VAL LAYS IT ACROSS THE PATH OF AN APPROACHING SEARCHER.

TRIPS THE HORSE AND LEAPS UPON THE BEWILDERED SOLDIER.

SWIFT AND SILENT AS THE SWOOP OF A HAWK THE DEADLY WORK IS DONE.

VAL DONS THE DEAD KNAVE'S ARMOR AND FRAYING A PIECE OF ROPE ATTACHES IT TO HIS LIP WITH BALSAM TO COMPLETE HIS DISGUISE.

BOLDLY HE RIDES AMONG HIS PURSUERS AND ANNOUNCES HIS OWN DEATH, SHOWING SWORD, BELT AND HELMET AS PROOF.

· NEXT WEEK ·
PERILOUS WORK

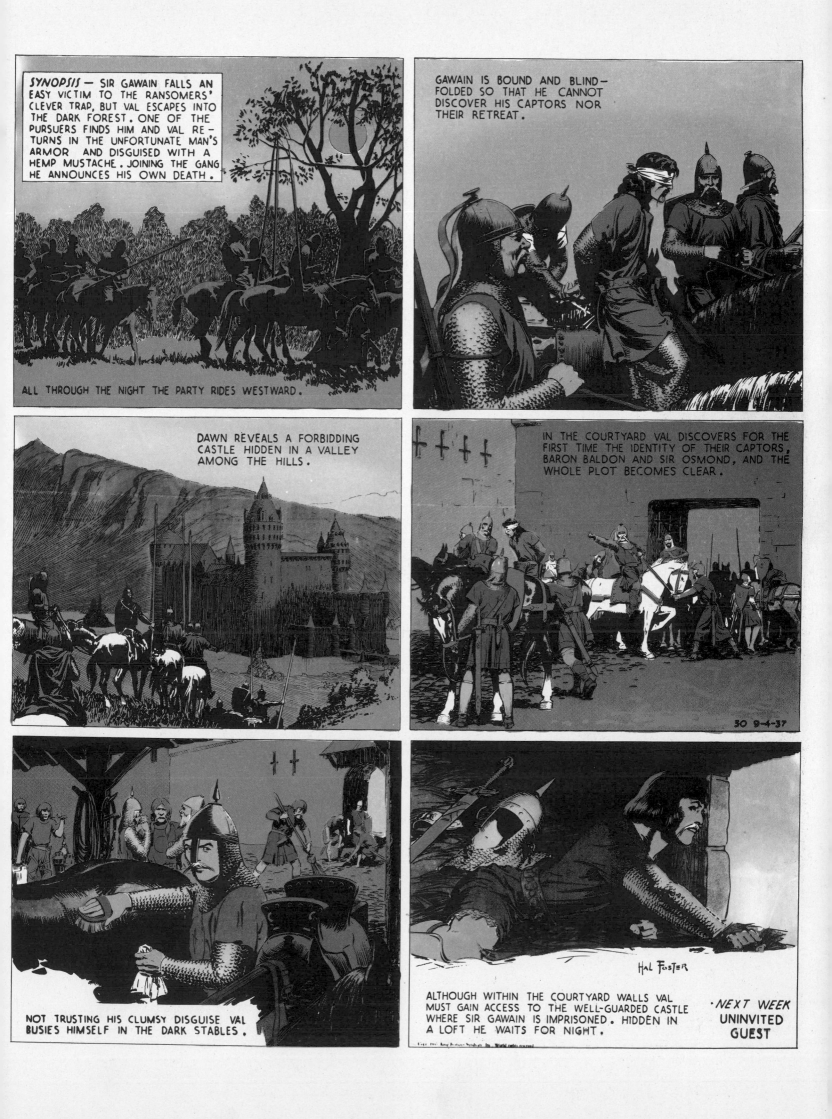

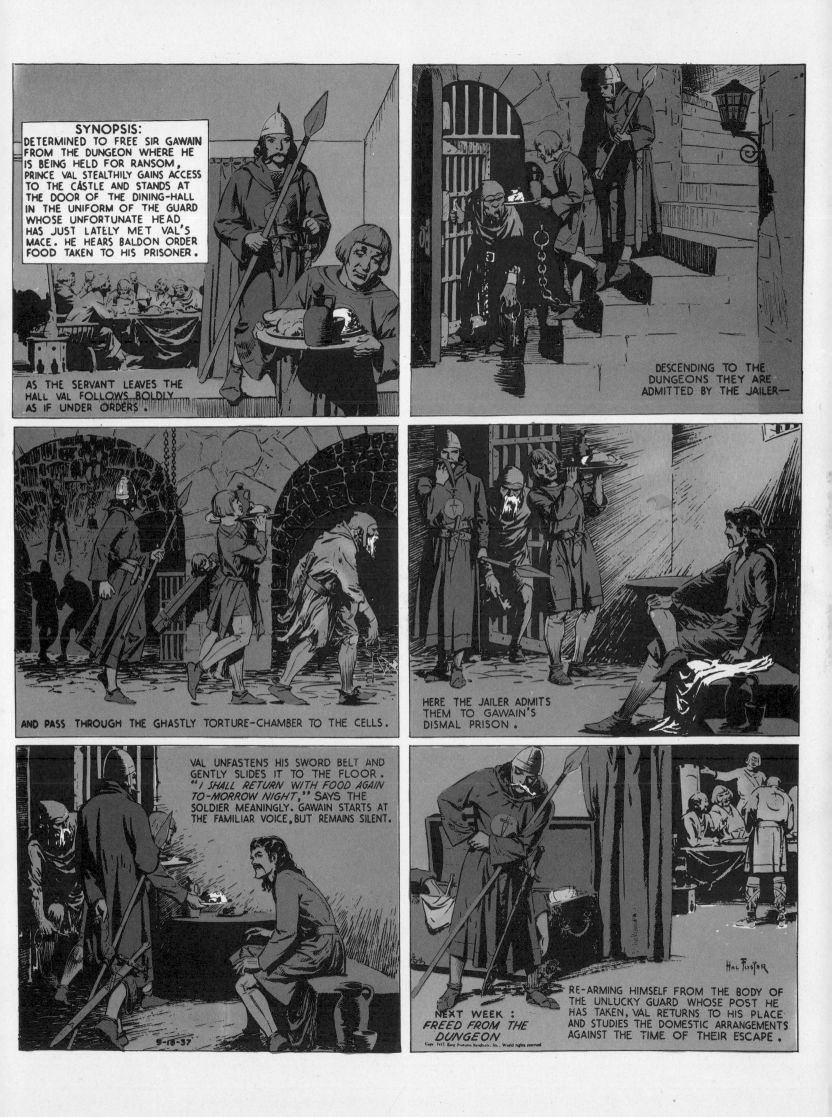

SYNOPSIS — DISGUISED AS A GUARD, PRINCE VAL ENTERS THE CASTLE WHERE HIS FRIEND, SIR GAWAIN, IS BEING HELD PRISONER IN A RANSOM PLOT. VAL MANAGES TO GET WEAPONS INTO HIS CELL AND PROMISES TO RETURN THE FOLLOWING NIGHT.

FINDING A COMFORTABLE PLACE, VAL HIDES THROUGH-OUT THE DAY AND LAYS CAREFUL PLANS FOR THE RESCUE.

"TWO SOLDIERS HAVE BEEN KILLED WITHIN THE CASTLE AND ANOTHER IS MISSING, SIR!" VAL'S NECESSARY ROUGHNESS OF THE NIGHT BEFORE IS REPORTED.

WHEN THE TIME COMES FOR GAWAIN'S FOOD TO BE TAKEN TO HIM, VAL DONS HIS DISGUISE AND LEAVES HIS HIDING-PLACE TO FOLLOW BOLDLY AS BEFORE.

WHEN THE BRUTAL JAILER UNBOLTS THE CELL DOOR VAL SAYS, "SIR GAWAIN, DON'T YOU THINK BOTH THE JAILER AND THE SERVANT HAVE OUTLIVED THEIR USEFULNESS?"

"YES," SAYS THE KNIGHT, THINKING PLEASANTLY OF FREEDOM, AND THEY REMEDY THE SITUATION NEATLY.

LEAVING THE DUNGEONS, THEY LOCK THE PONDEROUS DOORS AND TWIST THE KEYS OFF IN THE LOCKS TO DELAY DISCOVERY, THEN ASCEND INTO THE DANGEROUS CASTLE.

HAL FOSTER

NEXT WEEK— THE BARON'S GUESTS

53 9-26-37

SYNOPSIS:
SLAYING THE JAILERS, VAL AND GAWAIN ESCAPE FROM THE DUNGEON AND ASCEND UNDER COVER OF THE GREAT NOISE FROM THE BANQUET HALL TO THE SLEEPING-QUARTERS HIGH IN THE CASTLE.

THEY TAKE REFUGE IN THE BARON'S SLEEPING-APARTMENT.

AND ENJOY ALL THE LUXURIES OF HIS FINE APPOINTMENTS AND THE SERVICES OF HIS VALET.

A DINNER IS ORDERED.

AND THEN A FEW HOURS OF MUCH-NEEDED REST IN THE BARON'S GREAT BED.

AT DAWN THE SOUNDS OF REVELRY DIE AWAY IN THE BANQUET HALL AND THEY MAKE THEIR WAY TO THE ROOF WHERE VAL'S ROPE LIES.

THERE HE EXPLAINS TO GAWAIN HIS DARING PLAN OF ESCAPE AND SLIDES DOWN TO THE COURTYARD WALL.

VAL IS SOON DISCOVERED, THE ALARM IS SOUNDED AND THE SLEEPY SOLDIERS SWARM OUT TO MAKE AN EASY CAPTURE.

NEXT WEEK — *THE GREAT DIVE*

HAL FOSTER

34 10-2-37

SYNOPSIS — WITH COOL NERVE AND FLIMSY DISGUISE, VAL PENETRATES TO THE DUNGEONS AND LIBERATES SIR GAWAIN AND THEY ASCEND THROUGH THE DANGEROUS CASTLE TO THE ROOF WHILE A DRUNKEN REVEL IS BEING HELD.

IN THE DAWN LIGHT VAL IS DISCOVERED ON THE PARAPET AND IN THE CONFUSION GAWAIN SLIDES UNNOTICED FROM THE CASTLE ROOF TO THE COURTYARD BELOW—

AND IN THE DIM STABLES SADDLES TWO HORSES!

VAL IS TRAPPED AND THE SOLDIERS ARE CLOSING IN TO MAKE AN EASY CAPTURE—

BUT VAL STEPS UPON THE PARAPET AND BEFORE THEIR ASTONISHED EYES LEAPS FROM THE DIZZY HEIGHTS INTO THE MOAT BELOW.

35 10-9-37

LOWERING THE DRAWBRIDGE THEY SWARM OUT TO SEARCH THE MOAT.

AND SIR GAWAIN THUNDERS OUT TO FREEDOM!

A TROOP OF HORSEMEN GALLOPS IN PURSUIT.

HAL FOSTER

BUT THE WATCHERS ON THE WALL WAIT IN VAIN FOR VAL TO RE-APPEAR FROM THE MURKY WATERS.

NEXT WEEK— *BENEATH THE MOAT*

SYNOPSIS:
THE BARON BALDON AND SIR OSMOND ARE MAD WITH RAGE AND FEAR AS SIR GAWAIN ESCAPES FROM THEIR STRONG CASTLE AND SPEEDS TO KING ARTHUR WITH NEWS OF THEIR VILLAINY. EVERY EFFORT IS BEING MADE TO RE-CAPTURE HIM. VAL, WHO EFFECTED HIS ESCAPE, HAS PLUNGED INTO THE MOAT AND THEY WATCH FOR HIM TO RE-APPEAR IN VAIN.

FOR HOURS SOLDIERS WATCH THE MURKY WATERS BUT SEE NO SIGN OF VAL'S BODY.

THOUGH PARTLY STUNNED BY THE GREAT PLUNGE, VAL KEEPS HIS PLAN IN MIND AND SWIMS UNDER WATER—

TO THE FRINGE OF REEDS BENEATH THE CASTLE WALL, STIRRING THE MUD TO RENDER HIS MOVEMENTS INVISIBLE. THERE HE CUTS A HOLLOW REED.

LYING IN THE MUDDY SHALLOWS AND BREATHING THROUGH THE REED, HE WAITS FOR THE SEARCHERS TO GROW WEARY.

36 10-16-37

WITH INFINITE PAINS HE ARRANGES A SCREEN OF RUSHES AND SLOWLY LIFTS HIS HEAD--AT LAST HE CAN BREATHE WITH EASE AND WATCH THE SOLDIERS AT THEIR SEARCHING.

AT LAST THE WEARY DAY ENDS AND IN THE DARKNESS A DRIPPING FIGURE EMERGES FROM THE WATER TO GO IN SEARCH OF THE WAITING GAWAIN.

HAL FOSTER

NEXT WEEK— *GAWAIN WOUNDED*

SYNOPSIS - UNDER COVER OF NIGHT PRINCE VAL CRAWLS FROM THE MOAT WHERE HE HAS LAIN IN HIDING THROUGH THE DAY AND GOES IN SEARCH OF SIR GAWAIN. THEIR CAPTURE MEANS DEATH. THEIR ESCAPE WOULD BRING RUIN AND DEATH TO SIR OSMOND AND BARON BALDON - FROM FAR AND NEAR COME SOUNDS OF FRANTIC SEARCH.

VAL SOON STUMBLES UPON AN UNMISTAKABLE SIGN LEFT BY THE LIGHT-HEARTED GAWAIN.

LEAVING THE PATH AND GOING IN THE DIRECTION THE SIGN HAD INDICATED, VAL ENTERS A FOREST GLADE ——

AND FINDS GALLANT SIR GAWAIN LYING THERE TERRIBLY WOUNDED.

VAL'S SURGERY IS ROUGH AND PAINFUL, BUT THE GAPING WOUND IS CLEANSED AND CLOSED.

BY EASY STAGES THEY RIDE SOUTHWARD.

VAL'S ETERNAL VIGILANCE ENABLES THEM TO AVOID EVERY SEARCHING PARTY.

HAL FOSTER

AT LAST THEY SEE CAMELOT IN THE DISTANCE AND BELOW THEM A GREAT TOURNAMENT BEING HELD ON WINCHESTER HEATH.

• NEXT WEEK •
THE KING'S RAGE

The Ogre

HAROLD R FOSTER

SYNOPSIS:
THE TOURNAMENT OF THE QUEEN'S DIAMONDS ON WINCHESTER HEATH IS HALTED AS PRINCE VALIANT AND THE SWOONING SIR GAWAIN RIDE UP TO KING ARTHUR'S PAVILION AND THE ADVENTURE OF THE RANSOM PLOT IS FINISHED. THIS WAS BUT A MILD ADVENTURE AND IT WAS NECESSARY TO KILL ONLY SEVEN ENEMIES IN THE WAY OF BUSINESS. THE ONLY SERIOUS HAPPENING WAS THE WOUNDING OF SIR GAWAIN.

KING ARTHUR IS WROTH WHEN HE HEARS OF THE PERFIDY OF HIS TWO TRUSTED KNIGHTS, SIR OSMOND AND THE BARON BALDON.

"THE TOURNAMENT ENDS IN FAVOR OF MORE SERIOUS COMBAT," SAYS THE WARRIOR KING, AND STRAIGHTWAY LEADS HIS KNIGHTS NORTHWARD TO PUNISH THE RENEGADES.

SIR GAWAIN IS HEALING QUICKLY, TENDED BY MORGAN TODD, THE KING'S OWN PHYSICIAN —

38 10-30-37

HAL FOSTER

WHILE FAR AWAY A SLIM GIRL FRANTICALLY URGES A GREAT WAR-HORSE TOWARD THE NOW DESERTED CAMELOT.

· NEXT WEEK ·
THE
MAID ILENE

SYNOPSIS: WITH REST AND CARE SIR GAWAIN'S WOUND IS HEALING RAPIDLY-- ONE MORNING WHILE WATCHING YOUNG PRINCE VAL AT HIS TRAINING--

A SLIM GIRL URGES HER SPENT HORSE THROUGH THE MERLIN GATE.

THE MEN-AT-ARMS HELP HER DISMOUNT AND CONDUCT HER TO THE STEWARD. SHE TELLS A TALE OF INJUSTICE AND VIOLENCE AND ASKS FOR REDRESS, BUT IN ALL CAMELOT THERE IS BUT ONE KNIGHT, THE WOUNDED SIR GAWAIN.

THE MAID REPEATS HER TALE TO SIR GAWAIN, -- IN VAL'S DARK EYES THERE COMES A LOOK OF WONDER.

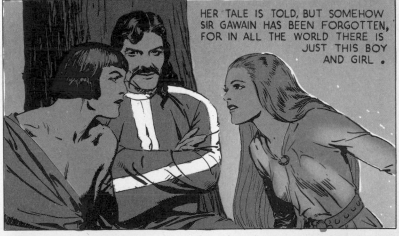

HER TALE IS TOLD, BUT SOMEHOW SIR GAWAIN HAS BEEN FORGOTTEN, FOR IN ALL THE WORLD THERE IS JUST THIS BOY AND GIRL.

SUDDENLY GAWAIN APPEARS CLAD ALL IN MAIL--"BUT SIR, YOU CANNOT TAKE THIS QUEST-YOUR WOUND-!" "I CAN ALWAYS LEAN ON YOU IN CASE OF NEED, VAL," SMILES THE KNIGHT.

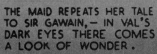

SO AGAIN THEY RIDE AT AD-VENTURE AND TO VAL THE WORLD IS A GLORIOUS PLACE BECAUSE OF THE BRIGHT FACE OF THE MAID ILENE.

· NEXT WEEK ·
THE PRINCE AND THE MAID ILENE

SYNOPSIS — "DESPITE A HALF-HEALED WOUND MY KNIGHT RIDES ON A QUEST. PRAY SIR, DO NOT DELAY US WITH A USELESS QUARREL." — THE RED KNIGHT LAUGHS EVILLY, "THEN YONDER FAIR MAID WILL FIND A STRONGER PROTECTOR IN ME!"

AND BEFORE PRINCE VALIANT CAN INTERFERE HE CHARGES.

THE WOUNDED SIR GAWAIN IS NO MATCH FOR THE RED KNIGHT, WHO THROWS HIM HEAVILY AND BURSTS OPEN THE WOUND AGAIN.

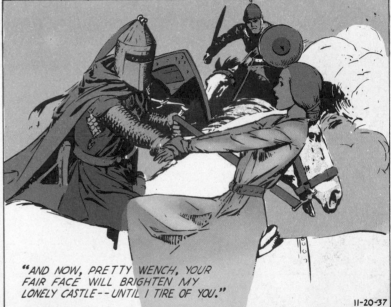

"AND NOW, PRETTY WENCH, YOUR FAIR FACE WILL BRIGHTEN MY LONELY CASTLE -- UNTIL I TIRE OF YOU."

11-20-37

WITH SUCH FEROCITY DOES VAL CHARGE TO THE RESCUE THAT BOTH HORSES AND RIDERS FALL HEADLONG!

FILLED WITH A COLD AND DEADLY FURY VAL FACES THE HARDENED VETERAN -- WILDCAT TO BULL THEY COMMENCE THE BATTLE FROM WHICH BUT ONE CAN EMERGE ALIVE.

NEXT WEEK
DEATH LOOKS ON

SYNOPSIS — RIDING AT ADVENTURE TO LIBERATE THE IMPRISONED PARENTS OF THE MAID ILENE, SIR GAWAIN AND VAL ARE HALTED BY A RED KNIGHT WHO CLAIMS THE FAIR-HAIRED GIRL.
WEAKENED BY HIS RECENT WOUND, SIR GAWAIN IS NO MATCH FOR HIS RED ADVERSARY AND IS THROWN HEAVILY. BUT NO ONE CAN HARM ILENE WHILE PRINCE VALIANT STILL BREATHES AND THE RED KNIGHT IS SURPRISED TO FIND THE YOUTHFUL SQUIRE CONFRONTING HIM.

VAL MEETS STRENGTH WITH AGILITY AND STRIVES TO TIRE HIS POWERFUL FOE BY CAUSING HIM TO SWING WILDLY.

NOTING THE SET OF THE RED KNIGHT'S SHIELD, VAL BANGS IT VICIOUSLY AGAIN AND AGAIN AGAINST HIS ADVERSARY'S CHIN.

TO BRACE HIMSELF AGAINST THESE JARRING SHOCKS, THE WEARY KNIGHT PLANTS HIS LEGS WIDE APART AND STRIVES TO CRUSH HIS AGILE FOE WITH A MIGHTY BLOW.

HAVING WORKED HIS MAN INTO POSITION, VAL ACTS WITH THE SPEED OF LIGHT AND THE RED WARRIOR COMES CRASHING DOWN.

VAL RIPS THE LACINGS FROM HIS HELM AND HIS THIRSTY DAGGER BRINGS SAFETY TO THE MAID ILENE.

HAL FOSTER   11-27-37

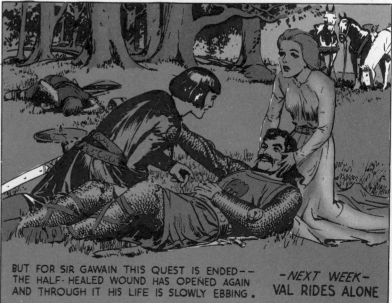

BUT FOR SIR GAWAIN THIS QUEST IS ENDED—THE HALF-HEALED WOUND HAS OPENED AGAIN AND THROUGH IT HIS LIFE IS SLOWLY EBBING.

—NEXT WEEK—
VAL RIDES ALONE

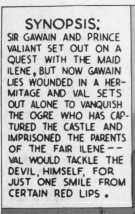

SYNOPSIS:
SIR GAWAIN AND PRINCE VALIANT SET OUT ON A QUEST WITH THE MAID ILENE, BUT NOW GAWAIN LIES WOUNDED IN A HERMITAGE AND VAL SETS OUT ALONE TO VANQUISH THE OGRE WHO HAS CAPTURED THE CASTLE AND IMPRISONED THE PARENTS OF THE FAIR ILENE — — VAL WOULD TACKLE THE DEVIL, HIMSELF, FOR JUST ONE SMILE FROM CERTAIN RED LIPS.

DESPITE THE SINISTER WARNING, VAL BLOWS A LUSTY BLAST ON THE GREAT HORN HANGING FROM THE CASTLE GATE.

SLOWLY THE GATE GOES UP AND A HOARSE VOICE CRIES, "*WHAT FOOL SEEKS THE DEADLY SOCIETY OF THE OGRE OF SINSTAR WOOD ?*"

STEPPING ASIDE, THE OGRE MOTIONS TO HIS WAITING HORSEMEN TO BRING IN THE IMPUDENT YOUTH.

BUT THE LIGHTLY-ARMED PRINCE QUICKLY OUT—DISTANCES HIS HEAVY PURSUERS AND, CIRCLING, FINDS A HIDING-PLACE OVERLOOKING THE CASTLE.

NOW IT SEEMED TO VAL THAT THE FEARFUL APPEARANCE OF THE OGRE WAS TOO THEATRICAL TO BE TRUE AND HE GETS A BRIGHT IDEA.

"*SO, THE OGRE RULES BY FEAR. WELL, TWO CAN PLAY AT THAT GAME,*" AND VAL PREPARES TO ENTER THE CASTLE IN THE DARK.

NEXT WEEK- *THE CASTLE WALL*

12-11-37

SYNOPSIS: FOR THE SAKE OF FAIR ILENE VAL DARES PIT HIS NIMBLE WIT AGAINST THE MIGHT OF THE OGRE OF SINSTAR WOOD AND ALL HIS FOLLOWERS. HE STUDIES THE CASTLE WALL AND FORMS HIS PLAN OF ENTRANCE.

WHEN NIGHT FALLS THE FEARLESS YOUTH DOFFS ALL HIS ARMOR SAVE ONLY A KNIFE AND SOFTLY ENTERS THE DARK MOAT.

SWIMMING UNDER WATER HE CAPTURES A LARGE GOOSE.

AT A SPOT WHERE TWO BUTTRESSES ARE CLOSE TOGETHER VAL LANDS AND CUTS HIS STAFFS TO THE PROPER LENGTH.

WEDGING THEM CAREFULLY AGAINST THE ROUGH STONES HE SLOWLY MOUNTS THE DIZZY HEIGHTS.

AVOIDING THE FIERCE WARRIORS GUARDING THE WALLS, VAL FINDS A SECLUDED SPOT ON THE ROOF.

12-18-37

FROM THE CAPTURED GOOSE VAL STARTS WORK ON A MASK THAT WILL MAKE HIM THE MOST FEARFUL SIGHT OUTSIDE OF HADES.
• NEXT WEEK •
TERROR MEETS TERROR

SYNOPSIS:
PRINCE VALIANT HAS UNDERTAKEN, SINGLE-HANDED, THE TASK OF VANQUISHING THE OGRE OF SIN-STAR WOOD. THE OGRE'S APPEARANCE IS SO FRIGHTFUL THAT VAL FIGURES ANYONE WHO MAKES HIMSELF HORRIBLE MUST BE OVERLY CONSCIOUS OF HORROR AND PLANS TO FIGHT FIRE WITH FIRE.

DESCENDING HIS ROPE, VAL SEARCHES EVERY LIGHTED WINDOW UNTIL HE FINDS THE OGRE'S CHAMBER.

THEN MOUNTING TO THE ROOF AGAIN DONS THE MASK HE HAS FASHIONED FROM A GOOSE.—WITH QUILLS HE MAKES TUSKS——

AND THE HORRID YELLOW SKIN IS PULLED OVER HIS HEAD AND PADDED HERE AND THERE WITH FEATHERS.

SLIDING DOWN TO THE OGRE'S WINDOW, HE SPRINGS FAR OUT, GIVES A PIERCING SHRIEK——

AND INTO THE OGRE'S ROOM FLIES A DEMON RIDING A STAFF!

"YOU HAVE FAIRLY EARNED A PLACE IN HELL," SCREAMS THE DEMON, "WHEN I RETURN IT WILL BE TO TAKE YOUR SOUL TO MY MASTER."

AND LEAPING TO THE WINDOW, FLIES OUT INTO THE NIGHT!

IN THE DARK THE OGRE CAN NOT SEE THE ROPE, VAL TURNS IN THE AIR AND SWINGS BACK.

"AND SO MY MASTER BIDS ME RETURN FOR YOU." LAUGHING HIDEOUSLY, THE DEMON COMES SOFTLY TOWARD ITS GASPING VICTIM.

12-25-37

HAL FOSTER

WITH A CHOKING MOAN THE OGRE SLOWLY SINKS TO THE FLOOR AND THE HEART THAT KNEW NO MERCY FOR OTHERS CEASED BEATING THROUGH SHEER TERROR.

NEXT WEEK-*THE HAUNTED CASTLE*

SYNOPSIS:
WITH HIS HORRIBLE MASK PRINCE VALIANT HAS FRIGHTENED THE OUTLAWS INTO PANIC. RUSHING TO THEIR FEARFUL LEADER THEY FIND THE OGRE UNWOUNDED, BUT STONE DEAD.

A TERROR WHO CAN BRING DEATH THUS IS MORE THAN EVEN THESE HARDENED OUTLAWS CAN STAND.

AND SOON THE MORE TIMID ARE HURRYING FROM THE GLOOMY CASTLE.

AS DAY DAWNS VAL WATCHES THE GROWING PANIC WITH SATISFACTION.

SOON THE WHOLE BAND IS RUSHING MADLY FROM THE HAUNTED CASTLE.

LOOKING BACK THEY CAN SEE AN OMINOUS BLACK FIGURE WATCHING THEIR FLIGHT.

"*THAT'S THAT!*" SAYS VAL, QUITE PLEASED WITH THE SUCCESS OF HIS TRICK AND REMOVES THE OILY GOOSESKIN MASK.

NEXT WEEK— "CORNERED"

HAL FOSTER 48 1-8-38

SYNOPSIS:
THINKING ALL THE OUTLAWS HAD FLED IN TERROR, VAL REMOVES THE HORRIBLE MASK, BUT TWO HARDY RUFFIANS, DELAYED BY THEIR SEARCH FOR LOOT, DISCOVER HIM AND HIS TRICK.

THE ARMED THIEVES ADVANCE, GRINNING FIENDISHLY.

BEING UNARMED, VAL SEEKS SAFETY IN FLIGHT.

THE OUTLAWS CORNER HIM, BUT HE REMEMBERS HIS ROPE DANGLING OUTSIDE AND LEAPS FROM THE WINDOW—

SWINGS FAR OUT AND CLAMBERS UPWARD.

ONE RUNS TO THE ROOF WHILE THE OTHER WAITS AT THE WINDOW.

1-15-38

AND DEATH COMES VERY CLOSE TO THE YOUNG PRINCE AS HE SWINGS BACK AND FORTH HELPLESSLY.

—NEXT WEEK—
"THE HUMAN TARGET"

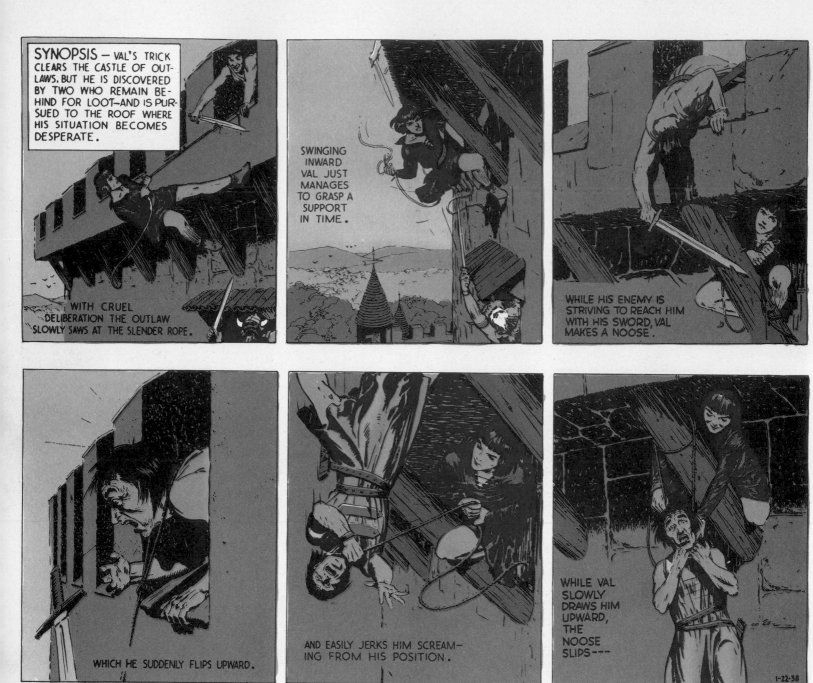

SYNOPSIS — VAL'S TRICK CLEARS THE CASTLE OF OUTLAWS. BUT HE IS DISCOVERED BY TWO WHO REMAIN BEHIND FOR LOOT—AND IS PURSUED TO THE ROOF WHERE HIS SITUATION BECOMES DESPERATE.

WITH CRUEL DELIBERATION THE OUTLAW SLOWLY SAWS AT THE SLENDER ROPE.

SWINGING INWARD VAL JUST MANAGES TO GRASP A SUPPORT IN TIME.

WHILE HIS ENEMY IS STRIVING TO REACH HIM WITH HIS SWORD, VAL MAKES A NOOSE.

WHICH HE SUDDENLY FLIPS UPWARD.

AND EASILY JERKS HIM SCREAMING FROM HIS POSITION.

WHILE VAL SLOWLY DRAWS HIM UPWARD, THE NOOSE SLIPS---

1-22-38

--AND THE CAPTIVE PLUNGES TO THE GROUND.

BUT THE SECOND OUTLAW HAS REACHED THE COURTYARD AND SHOUTS UPWARD, "HERE'S HOW WE HUNT SQUIRRELS IN SINSTAR WOODS."

HAL FOSTER

"POOR SQUIRRELS," MUTTERS VAL, WONDERING HOW LONG HE CAN DODGE THESE WHISTLING MESSENGERS OF DEATH

NEXT WEEK — THE DUEL OF WITS

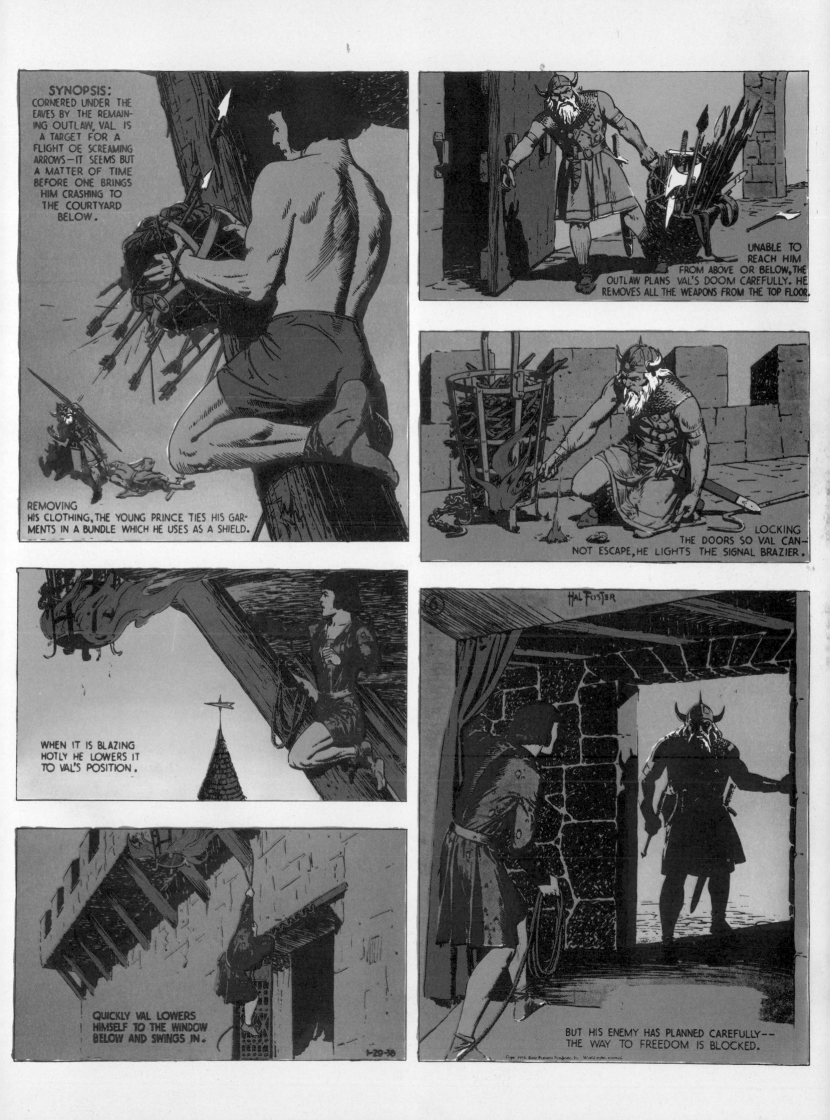

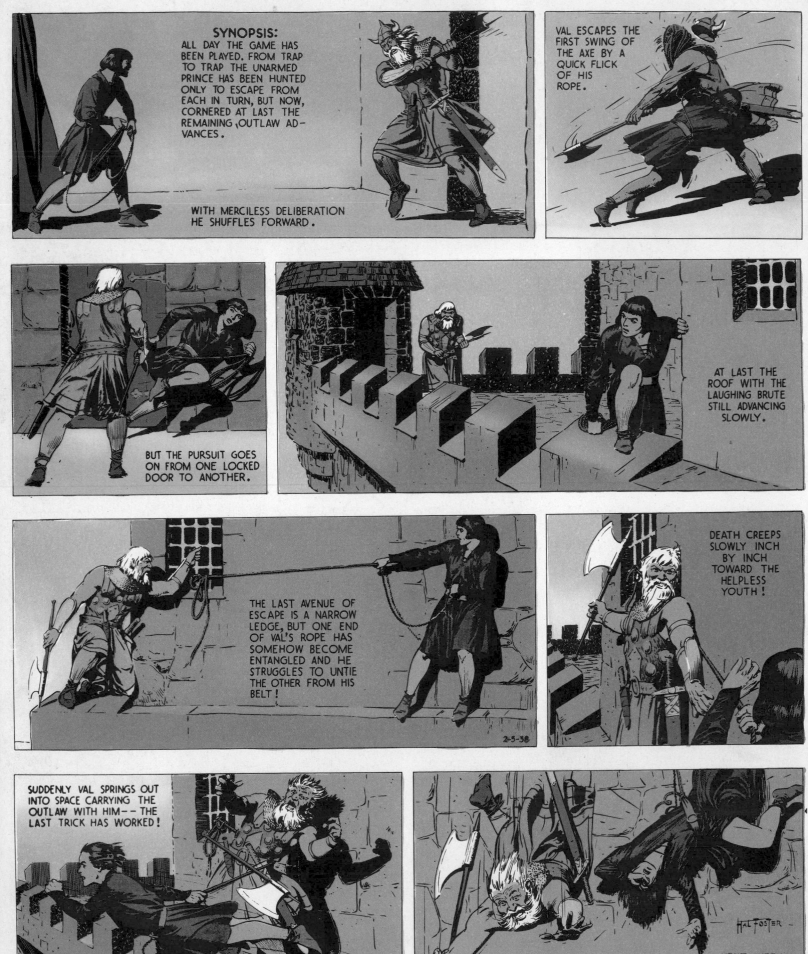

SYNOPSIS: WEARING A HORRIBLE MASK, PRINCE VAL HAS FRIGHTENED ALL THE OUTLAWS FROM THE CASTLE EXCEPT TWO. THESE HARDY RUFFIANS CHASE THE UNARMED PRINCE TO THE ROOF WHERE THEY ARE TRICKED TO THEIR DOOM BY A PIECE OF ROPE.

AFTER A TREMENDOUS STRUGGLE THE HALF-CONSCIOUS YOUTH GAINS THE ROOF.

FINDING AN IRON BAR, VAL SMASHES THE LOCKED DOORS AND ENTERS THE NOW-DESERTED CASTLE.

AS THE LAST OUTLAW HURTLES TO THE YARD BELOW VAL CRASHES WITH STUNNING FORCE AGAINST THE WALL.

AFTER A WEARY SEARCH HE DISCOVERS THE KEYS TO THE DUNGEONS.

AND THE YOUNG PRINCE IS ABLE TO LIBERATE ILENE'S FATHER, THE THANE OF BRANWYN, WHO HAS BEEN IMPRISONED SINCE THE OGRE'S CAPTURE OF THE CASTLE.

THE DUNGEON CELLS ALSO GIVE UP THE REST OF THE THANE'S FAMILY AND RETAINERS.

THE TENDER HEART OF ILENE BEATS WILDLY WHEN THE MESSENGER ARRIVES WITH THE NEWS OF VAL'S HEROIC DEEDS AND SHE HASTENS TO RETURN.

NEXT WEEK · CUPID USES AN AXE

VAL'S FIRST THOUGHT IS FOR THE MAID, ILENE, AND HE TELLS THE THANE OF THE HERMITAGE WHERE SHE IS WAITING.

THREE DAYS OF HARDSHIP WITH NEITHER FOOD NOR SLEEP HAVE TAKEN THEIR TOLL AND, HIS WORK DONE, THE YOUTHFUL PRINCE COLLAPSES.

"PRINCE VALIANT HAS SUCCEEDED, OH! ISN'T HE WONDERFUL?" SINGS THE MAID ILENE AS SHE HURRIEDLY BIDS GOOD-BY TO SIR GAWAIN AND THE HERMIT.

VAL REGALES THE THANE WITH THE STORY OF HOW HE TRICKED THE OGRE TO HIS DOOM WITH A GOOSE-SKIN MASK.

BUT ON THE MORROW HIS SOLE OCCUPATION IS GAZING UP THE SUNLIT ROAD BY WHICH ILENE WILL SOON COME RIDING HOMEWARD.

AND THEN SHE COMES, RIDING GAYLY THROUGH THE SPRING WOODS AND VAL'S HEART PLAYS STRANGE TRICKS.

THE OLD THANE AND HIS WIFE WARMLY GREET THE CHILD THEY HAD THOUGHT LOST.

"IN A FEW DAYS SIR GAWAIN WILL BE STRONG ENOUGH TO BE BROUGHT HERE," SAYS ILENE AS THEY WANDER HAPPILY AFIELD.

A KINDLY MOON LOOKS DOWN ON AN OLD, OLD STORY THAT A BOY AND GIRL THINK IS NEW.

2-19-38
Copr. 1938. King Features Syndicate. Inc... World rights reserved.

HAL FOSTER

WHILE THE THANE AND HIS LADY GAZE AT A SIGNED PARCHMENT THAT IS TO CAUSE MUCH HEARTBREAK.
–NEXT WEEK–
"THE MARRIAGE CONTRACT"

The Fairy Morgana

SYNOPSIS— AFTER WRESTING BRANWYN CASTLE FROM THE OGRE AND RESTORING IT TO THE THANE, VAL BECOMES A PETTED HERO AND HIS CUP OF HAPPINESS IS FILLED TO OVERFLOWING WHEN SWEET ILENE GIVES HIM HER YOUNG HEART. "A POX ON THE WITCH'S DULL PROPHECY THAT I'D KNOW NO CONTENTMENT," LAUGHS VAL HAPPILY.

A CONVEYANCE IS DISPATCHED TO BRING THE WOUNDED SIR GAWAIN TO BRANWYN CASTLE.

NEXT AFTERNOON VAL IS SUMMONED TO THE THANE'S CHAMBER.

"YOU HAVE DONE ME A GREAT SERVICE, PRINCE VALIANT. ASK WHAT YOU WILL OF ME, EVEN TO A THIRD OF MY FIEF."

"I ASK A MORE PRECIOUS REWARD THAN ALL YOUR LANDS, NOBLE SIR, THE HAND OF YOUR DAUGHTER IN MARRIAGE."

"THE ONE GIFT I AM UNABLE TO GRANT YOU, FOR THE KING OF ORD HAS ASKED THAT SHE BECOME THE WIFE OF HIS SON, THE PRINCE AND THE MARRIAGE CONTRACT WAS SIGNED MONTHS AGO."

2-26-38

"MY BOY," SAYS THE WISE OLD THANE, "SHE WILL BE THE WIFE OF A WEALTHY PRINCE AND SOME DAY A STATELY QUEEN. IN THE SPLENDOR OF COURT LIFE SHE WILL FORGET THIS GIRLISH LOVE FOR A PENNILESS LAD. BESIDES, VAL," SAYS THE THANE LOWERING HIS VOICE, "SHE IS VERY MUCH LIKE HER MOTHER, A FINE WOMAN, BUT ASSERTIVE -- VERY ASSERTIVE."

THE SLEEPLESS BOY, GAZING AT THE WINDOW OF A SLEEPLESS MAID, VOWS — "WHO TAKES ILENE FROM ME MUST FIGHT AND FIGHT HARD."

BUT IN THE CHILL DAWN COMES A MESSENGER CRYING, "SIR GAWAIN IS GONE, CARRIED OFF BY A SORCERESS."

HAL FOSTER

• NEXT WEEK •
THE CHOICE

SYNOPSIS—WHEN THE MESSENGER BRINGS WORD THAT SIR GAWAIN HAS BEEN CARRIED OFF, PRINCE VALIANT IS TORN BETWEEN LOVE AND DUTY. SHALL HE FLY TO GAWAIN'S ASSISTANCE OR STAY AND FIGHT FOR SWEET ILENE ?

VAL FALTERED BUT AN INSTANT. "I SHALL RETURN," HE CRIES. "IN SPITE OF YOUR BETROTHAL TO PRINCE ARN I SHALL WIN YOU AND IN SPITE OF THE WITCH'S PROPHECY I SHALL KNOW CONTENTMENT."

AND MOUNTING HIS HORSE CLATTERS FROM THE CASTLE.

SO FAST DOES HE RIDE THAT ERE SUN-DOWN HE ARRIVES AT THE HERMITAGE .

THE HERMIT TELLS,—"A GREAT LADY PASSED AND SEEING SIR GAWAIN SLEEPING IN THE SUNLIGHT CAST A SPELL ON HIM AND CARRIED HIM AWAY." "'TWAS MORGAN LE FEY, HALF-SISTER OF THE KING, BEAUTIFUL, EVIL AND MIS-TRESS OF STRANGE MAGIC."

"I MUST RIDE TO HER CASTLE DOLOROUS GARDE AND RESCUE SIR GAWAIN."

REMOUNTED ON SIR GAWAIN'S GREAT HORSE VAL GALLOPS THROUGH THE NIGHT.

3-5-38

AND AT DAWN SEES FAR OUT IN THE MARSH THE SINISTER CASTLE THAT ALL MEN AVOID.

• NEXT WEEK •
THE SORCERESS

SYNOPSIS:
MORGAN LE FEY, BEAUTIFUL AND EVIL - HAS SECRETLY LOVED SIR GAWAIN. FINDING HIM RECOVERING FROM HIS WOUNDS IN A HERMITAGE, SHE CARRIES HIM OFF. VAL COMES TO THE RESCUE! EVEN THOUGH IT COSTS HIM HIS CHANCE OF WINNING THE MAID ILENE.

OVER THE CAUSEWAY THAT EXTENDS TO DOLOROUS GARDE- FAR OUT IN THE SWAMPS-GALLOPS THE ANXIOUS PRINCE

VAL BLOWS A RESOUNDING BLAST ON THE HORN THAT HANGS BY A CHAIN TO THE CURIOUSLY WROUGHT GATES.

THEY OPEN AND VAL ENTERS THE DREAD CASTLE, SILENTLY ESCORTED BY VERY UN-WHOLESOME-LOOKING ATTENDANTS.

THE LOVELY SORCERESS RECEIVES HIM GRACIOUSLY AND LISTENS TO HIS DEMAND FOR GAWAIN'S FREEDOM.

"YOUR SUSPICIONS WOUND ME, HANDSOME BOY, FOR I HAVE LOVED SIR GAWAIN THESE MANY YEARS AND HAVE ONLY BROUGHT HIM HERE THAT HIS WOUNDS MAY BE TENDERLY TREATED."

THEN SHE ASKS VAL TO TELL HER OF HIS ADVENTURES WITH SIR GAWAIN WHILE A SILENT ATTENDANT SERVES THEM WINE AND SWEET CAKES.

BUT THE WINE CONTAINS A SUBTLE DRUG AND AS HIS STRENGTH EBBS AWAY VAL HEARS A MOCKING LAUGH.

3-12-38

AND UPON THE HELPLESS YOUTH THE HYPNOTIC SORCERESS CASTS A POWERFUL SPELL.

NEXT WEEK — THE SPELL !

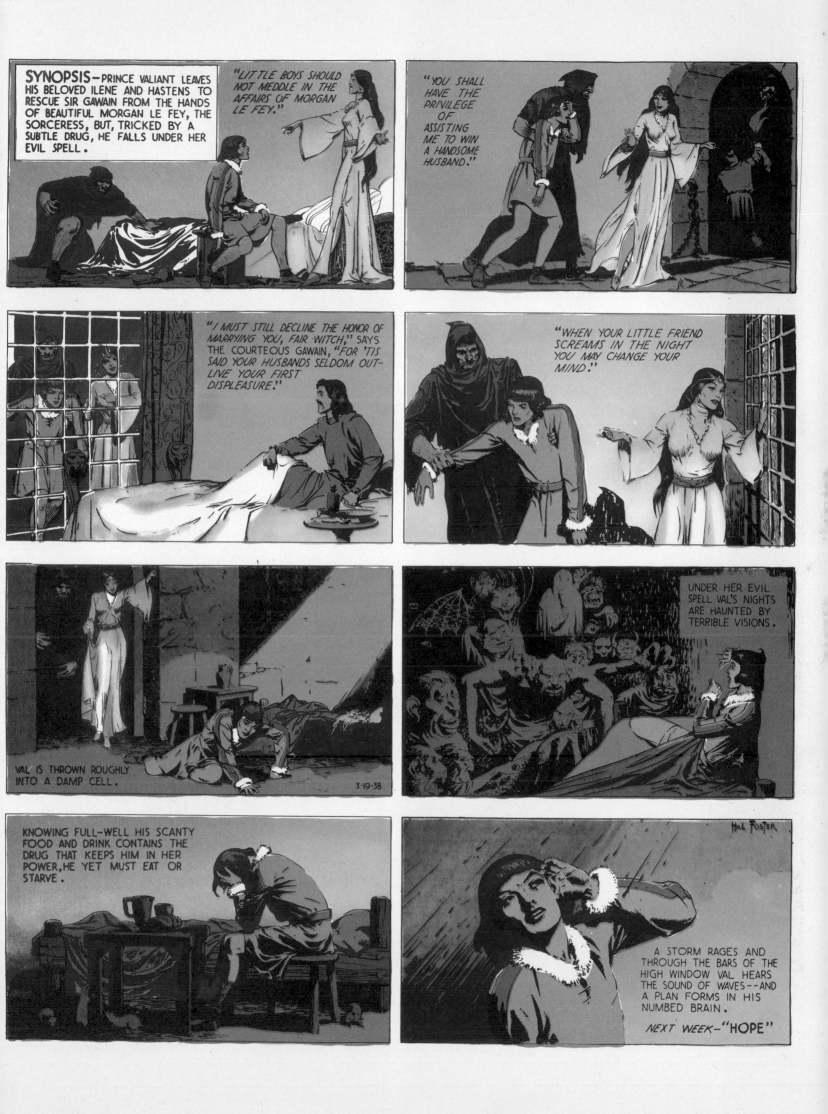

ENDEAVORING TO RESCUE SIR GAWAIN, VAL FALLS UNDER THE EVIL SPELL OF MORGAN LE FEY, THE SORCERESS. WEAKENED BY A DRUG GIVEN HIM IN HIS WINE, THE YOUNG PRINCE IS UNABLE TO ESCAPE HER WITCHERY.

DURING A STORM VAL HEARS THE SOUND OF WAVES BE- NEATH HIS BARRED WINDOW AND, REMOVING A SHOE—

TIES IT TO A RAVELING FROM HIS GARMENT AND THROWS IT THROUGH THE WINDOW.

"WATER! NOW IF THE DRUG IS GIVEN ME IN THE WINE I MAY YET BE SAVED."

WITH PLENTY OF WATER TO DRINK HE SPILLS THE DRUGGED WINE ON THE FLOOR AND FEIGNS WEAKNESS.

AS HIS STRENGTH RETURNS HE THROWS OFF THE SPELL AND SETS TO WORK, HIS ONLY TOOL IS A METAL BELT-BUCKLE.

IT IS MANY DAYS BEFORE HE SUCCEEDS IN DISLODG- ING THE STONE THAT HOLDS THE BARS IN PLACE.

ON A STORMY NIGHT HE ESCAPES AND REPLACES THE STONE AND BARS CAREFULLY— HE, TOO, LEAVES MYSTERY BEHIND!

3-26-38

THROUGH THE TREACHEROUS SWAMPS HE STRUGGLES TOWARD SHORE.

AND HEADS FOR CAMELOT, THIRTY MILES AWAY.

HAL FOSTER

NEXT WEEK-WISE MERLIN

SYNOPSIS: AFTER WEEKS OF HORROR IN THE GLOOMY CASTLE OF MORGAN LE FEY, THE SORCERESS, VAL ESCAPES ACROSS THE TREACHEROUS SWAMPS AND SETS OUT FOR CAMELOT TO GET ASSISTANCE IN SAVING SIR GAWAIN.

HOUR AFTER HOUR VAL TROTS DOGGEDLY ON THROUGH STORM AND DARKNESS.

IN THE EARLY DAWN HE SEES MERLIN'S TOWER IN THE DISTANCE. "ONE FIGHTS FIRE WITH FIRE; WHY NOT MAGIC WITH MAGIC?" AND VAL TURNS OFF TOWARD THE CASTLE.

IF ANYONE CAN HELP SIR GAWAIN IT IS WISE MERLIN, THE WIZARD, ADVISER TO KING ARTHUR.

THE WEARY, MUD-STAINED PRINCE IS ADMITTED TO MERLIN'S CHAMBER.

AFTER VAL TELLS HIS STORY, MERLIN SAYS—"SHE IS EVIL AND WILL MURDER GAWAIN AND CAST HIS BODY IN THE MARSH AT THE APPROACH OF ARMED FORCES. WE MUST BE SUBTLE."

WHILE VAL RESTS MERLIN SEARCHES THROUGH HIS ANCIENT VOLUMES OF STRANGE LORE.

"I CAN HELP, BUT FIRST YOU MUST SECURE FOR ME SOMETHING THIS SORCERESS HAS WORN, OR HANDLED OR VALUED, THEN I CAN CAST A SPELL."

4-2-38

WELL-ARMED AND MOUNTED, VAL STARTS BACK ON HIS DANGEROUS MISSION—

HAL FOSTER

AND COMES IN SIGHT OF DOLOROUS GARDE" JUST AS A HUNTING PARTY EMERGES TO GO A-HAWKING

NEXT WEEK—PERILOUS SPORT

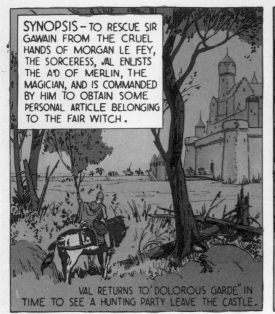

SYNOPSIS — TO RESCUE SIR GAWAIN FROM THE CRUEL HANDS OF MORGAN LE FEY, THE SORCERESS, VAL ENLISTS THE AID OF MERLIN, THE MAGICIAN, AND IS COMMANDED BY HIM TO OBTAIN SOME PERSONAL ARTICLE BELONGING TO THE FAIR WITCH.

VAL RETURNS TO "DOLOROUS GARDE" IN TIME TO SEE A HUNTING PARTY LEAVE THE CASTLE.

MORGAN LE FEY AND HER FRIENDS GO A-HAWKING. VAL FOLLOWS AT A DISTANCE.

FROM A PLACE OF CONCEALMENT, VAL SEES LE FEY RELEASE HER FAVORITE FALCON.

THE FALCON PURSUES ITS QUARRY IN VAL'S DIRECTION.

"THAT HAWK IS THE PERSONAL POSSESSION OF MORGAN LE FEY'S THAT I SEEK. HERE GOES!"

FLASHING ACROSS THE MEADOW HE GRASPS THE BIRD BEFORE IT LANDS.

WHEELING ABOUT, VAL SETS SPURS TO HIS MOUNT. WITH A SHOUT OF RAGE THE HUNTERS RACE IN PURSUIT.

REACHING MERLIN TOWER, VAL POUNDS UPON THE DOOR, WHILE THE ANGRY HUNTERS CLOSE IN SWIFTLY

GRIPPING HIS PRIZE TIGHTLY, VAL LASHES OUT WITH HIS SWORD AND, FOR A TIME, HOLDS BACK HIS ATTACKERS.

HAL FOSTER

NEXT WEEK — *MERLIN'S CONJURING*

SYNOPSIS—VAL APPEALS TO MERLIN, THE GREAT MAGICIAN, FOR AID IN RESCUING SIR GAWAIN FROM THE POWER OF MORGAN LE FEY, THE SORCERESS. MERLIN ASKS FOR SOME PERSONAL POSSESSION OF LE FEY'S WITH WHICH TO WORK HIS MAGIC AND VAL STEALS HER PET FALCON, BUT SO SWIFT IS THE PURSUIT THAT HE IS CORNERED AT MERLIN'S GATE.

SHOUTING LUSTILY FOR HELP, VAL HOLDS OFF THE ANGRY HUNTSMEN.

HELP COMES UNEXPECTEDLY.

MERLIN APPROVES OF VAL'S SOUVENIR.

MORGAN LE FEY IS FILLED WITH DREAD WHEN SHE HEARS WHO STOLE HER FALCON AND TO WHOM IT WAS TAKEN.

WISE MERLIN SETS TO WORK ON A MAGIC THAT WILL FORCE SIR GAWAIN'S RELEASE.

WHILE VAL WANDERS IN THE GREAT MAGICIAN'S ENCHANTED GARDEN.

BUT EVEN THE STRANGE ILLUSIONS THAT FILL THIS TWILIGHT PLACE CANNOT TURN HIS THOUGHTS FROM FAIR ILENE.

MIDNIGHT; AND INTO THE BEDCHAMBER OF LE FEY THERE COME CRAWLING STRANGE FANTASIES CONJURED UP FROM THE HALF-WORLD BY MERLIN.

NEXT WEEK—SIR GAWAIN IS FREED.

SYNOPSIS— TO FORCE MORGAN LE FEY, THE SORCERESS, TO RELEASE SIR GAWAIN, WHOM SHE IS HOLDING PRISONER, MERLIN CONJURES UP STRANGE TERRORS FROM THE HALF—WORLD OF DREAMS AND MAKES NIGHT HIDEOUS FOR HER.

NO MAGIC THAT SHE CAN DEVISE WILL KEEP BACK THE GHOSTLY HORRORS THAT MAKE HIDEOUS HER EVERY SLEEPING MOMENT.

"NOW GO TO MORGAN LE FEY AND SAY TO HER THAT SHE WILL KNOW NO REST UNTIL YOU AND SIR GAWAIN RETURN HERE SAFELY TO ME."

ARRIVING AT THE GATE OF 'DOLOROUS GARDE' PRINCE VALIANT IS QUIETLY SEIZED—

AND BROUGHT BEFORE THE RAGING SORCERESS BY HER QUEER SERVANTS.

GLADLY WOULD SHE CONDEMN THEM BOTH TO A LINGERING DEATH, BUT VAL REMINDS HER OF MERLIN'S THREAT.

SULLENLY SHE ORDERS SIR GAWAIN'S RELEASE.

"MY PRICELESS SQUIRE!" LAUGHS THE GRATIFIED GAWAIN, "YOU HAVE SAVED ME FROM PRISON; YOU HAVE SAVED ME FROM DEATH AND NOW, BLESS YOU, YOU SAVE ME FROM MATRIMONY!"

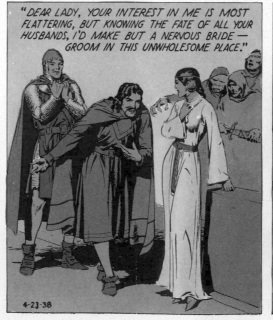

"DEAR LADY, YOUR INTEREST IN ME IS MOST FLATTERING, BUT KNOWING THE FATE OF ALL YOUR HUSBANDS, I'D MAKE BUT A NERVOUS BRIDE—GROOM IN THIS UNWHOLESOME PLACE."

4-23-38

AS THE LIGHT-HEARTED PAIR DEPART VAL LEAVES A TALISMAN TO HOLD BACK LE FEY'S STRANGE HENCHMEN.

HAL FOSTER

NEXT WEEK—*THE MESSENGER*

SYNOPSIS—AIDED BY MERLIN'S STRONG MAGIC, PRINCE VALIANT RESCUES SIR GAWAIN FROM "DOLOROUS GARDE", WHERE HE HAS BEEN IMPRISONED BY MORGAN LE FEY, THE SORCERESS. THAT HER STRANGE SERVITORS DARE NOT PASS. VAL'S CHARM IS EVIDENCE OF THE UNWHOLESOME REGION FROM WHICH SHE HAD RECRUITED THEM.

GAWAIN SINGS HAPPILY IN HIS NEW-FOUND FREEDOM, BUT THE YOUNG PRINCE HURRIES FORWARD ANXIOUSLY.

"YOU ARE UNHAPPY, VAL. IS THERE ANY—THING I CAN DO?" INTO HIS FRIEND'S SYMPATHETIC EAR VAL POURS HIS TALE OF WOE—

—OF HOW ILENE HAS BEEN BETROTHED BY HER FATHER TO PRINCE ARN OF ORD.

"BUT SHE LOVES ONLY ME AND I MEAN TO HAVE HER FOR MY OWN IN SPITE OF HER FATHER, PRINCE ARN OR THE DEVIL, HIMSELF!"

THEY COME AT LAST TO MERLIN'S TOWER.

THE GRATEFUL PAIR THANK THEIR WISE HELPER.
4-30-38

"YOU MAY KEEP THE ARMS I LENT YOU TO USE IN GOOD KING ARTHUR'S SERVICE.'"

AS THEY NEAR CAMELOT THEY ARE JOINED BY A FELLOW TRAVELER WHO, UNKNOWN TO THEM, BEARS A MESSAGE THAT WILL CHANGE VAL'S WHOLE LIFE.

NEXT WEEK— WEDDING INVITATIONS

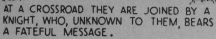

SYNOPSIS:— GAWAIN, THE LIGHT HEARTED, AND PRINCE VALIANT, HIS NIMBLE SQUIRE, HASTEN TO CAMELOT TO REPORT THE SUCCESS OF THEIR LATEST QUEST. EACH MINUTE SPENT AWAY FROM SWEET ILENE IS, TO VAL, A WEARY YEAR AND HE SPURS FORWARD SWIFTLY.

AT A CROSSROAD THEY ARE JOINED BY A KNIGHT, WHO, UNKNOWN TO THEM, BEARS A FATEFUL MESSAGE.

THE KNIGHTS OF THE ROUND TABLE WELCOME THEM BOISTEROUSLY, FOR THE MERRY GAWAIN AND HIS WITTY SQUIRE ARE GREAT FAVORITES.

A FEAST IS HELD IN THEIR HONOR.

KING ARTHUR RISES TO ANNOUNCE THAT A JOYOUS MESSAGE IS TO BE READ.

65 5-7-38

THE KNIGHT THEY HAD MET RIDING INTO CAMELOT ARISES AND READS—"THE KING OF ORD INVITES YOU ONE AND ALL TO A GREAT TOURNAMENT TO CELEBRATE THE MARRIAGE OF HIS SON, PRINCE ARN, TO ILENE OF BRANWYN."

IT IS A TERRIBLE BLOW TO VAL AND HIS HEART IS SICK WITH RAGE AND SORROW.

HE HIDES HIS BREAKING HEART AND THAT NIGHT NO ONE IS GAYER THAN THIS BRAVE AND MANLY PRINCE.

BUT WHEN THE LIGHTS GO OUT ONE BY ONE AND ALL IS SILENT IN THE GREAT CASTLE, IT IS ONLY A HURT BOY WHO QUIETLY SOBS OUT HIS HEARTBREAK IN THE DARK.

GAWAIN COVERS THE SLEEPING LAD WITH HIS SCARLET CLOAK.
NEXT WEEK—THE DISAPPEARANCE

Prince Arn

SYNOPSIS—WHILE THE FEAST IS AT ITS HEIGHT A MESSENGER PROCLAIMS THAT THE MARRIAGE OF PRINCE ARN TO THE GOLDEN-HAIRED ILENE WILL TAKE PLACE THE FOLLOWING WEEK. NO ONE BUT GAWAIN KNOWS HOW MUCH VAL LOVES THIS SLIM MAID. IN THE MORNING VAL HAS DISAPPEARED!

SIR GAWAIN SEARCHES ALL CAMELOT FOR HIS YOUNG FRIEND, BUT NOWHERE CAN HE BE FOUND.

FOR WITH THE DAWN'S LIGHT HAD COME RESOLUTION. VAL HAD DETERMINED TO SEEK PRINCE ARN AND FIGHT HIM FOR FAIR ILENE!

WELL-ARMED, VAL DEPARTS FROM CAMELOT IN THE EARLY MORN.

ANXIOUS TO FIND PRINCE ARN BEFORE THE WEDDING CAN TAKE PLACE, VAL RAGES IMPATIENTLY WHEN HIS PATH IS BLOCKED BY A QUESTING KNIGHT.

IN ACCORDANCE WITH CUSTOM, THE KNIGHT CHALLENGES TO A TILT — VAL SETS SHIELD AND LANCE AND—

HIS ANGER FLAMING AT THE DELAY, CHARGES WITH DEADLY FURY.

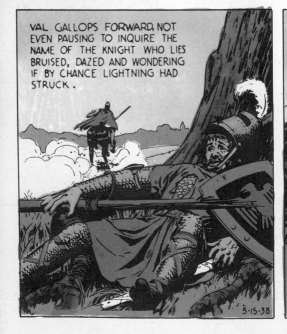

VAL GALLOPS FORWARD, NOT EVEN PAUSING TO INQUIRE THE NAME OF THE KNIGHT WHO LIES BRUISED, DAZED AND WONDERING IF BY CHANCE LIGHTNING HAD STRUCK.

5-15-38

RIDING TOWARD THE KINGDOM OF ORD, VAL FINDS AMPLE EVIDENCE THAT VIKING RAIDERS ARE AGAIN LAYING WASTE THE COASTS OF ENGLAND.

HAL FOSTER

VAL, GIVING NO HEED TO THE PRESENCE OF DANGER, ENTERS TOWARD A NARROW BRIDGE.

NEXT WEEK— *PRINCE ARN*

SYNOPSIS: WITH BUT ONE LANCE, ONE SWORD AND ONE SHIELD BETWEEN THEM, PRINCE VALIANT AND PRINCE ARN CANNOT CONTINUE THEIR DISPUTE AS TO WHO SHALL HAVE ILENE. SO TOGETHER THEY GO IN SEARCH OF ARMS.

"WE SHALL RIDE TOWARD BRANWYN TOGETHER BUT ONLY ONE OF US WILL FINISH THE JOURNEY."

"WE WILL BORROW WHAT WE NEED FROM YONDER BLACK KNIGHT."

"YOU MAY HELP YOURSELVES TO ANYTHING OF MINE YOU NEED IF EITHER OF YOU BE MAN ENOUGH TO TAKE IT!"

ARN WINS THE TOSS OF A COIN AND, TAKING VAL'S LANCE AND SHIELD, ADDRESSES THE STRANGER.

A THUNDERING OF HOOFS, A MIGHTY SHOCK AND THE BLACK KNIGHT GOES DOWN WITH A CRASH!

CALMLY THE TWO METTLESOME LADS ARM THEMSELVES AND PREPARE TO WIN EITHER ILENE OR DEATH.

"ILENE OR DEATH!" SHOUTS VAL. "DEATH OR ILENE!" CRIES ARN, AS THEY MEET FURIOUSLY.

THE STRUGGLE RAGES WHILE THE SUN DESCENDS HALF-WAY DOWN THE EVENING SKY AND STILL THE WEARY AND BLEEDING LADS FIGHT DOGGEDLY ON.

5-29-38

HAL FOSTER

A SHOUT FROM THE BLACK KNIGHT MAKES THEM PAUSE AND THERE, AT THE EDGE OF THE GLADE, IS A PARTY OF VIKING RAIDERS.

NEXT WEEK—ILENE ABDUCTED!

"TO HORSE," SHOUTS THE BLACK KNIGHT, "TO HORSE AND LET'S HAVE AT THEM!"

MOUNTING SWIFTLY, THEY SPUR THEIR GREAT WAR-HORSES INTO THE BAND OF BARBARIANS, SLASHING MIGHTILY RIGHT AND LEFT UNTIL THE VIKINGS BREAK AND FLEE WILDLY, LEAVING THEIR PRISONERS BEHIND.

"PRINCE VAL, FOR HEAVEN'S SAKE HELP US. WE WERE ESCORTING MISTRESS ILENE TO THE PALACE OF THE KING OF ORD WHEN WE WERE CAPTURED BY THE VIKINGS — THEY ARE TAKING HER TO THE COAST!"

"MOUNT, SIR KNIGHT, AND CARRY THIS NEWS TO GOOD KING ARTHUR AT CAMELOT —RIDE!"

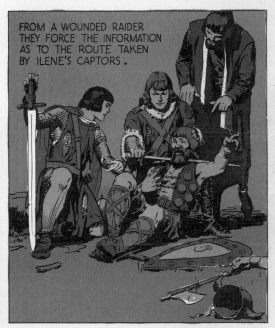

FROM A WOUNDED RAIDER THEY FORCE THE INFORMATION AS TO THE ROUTE TAKEN BY ILENE'S CAPTORS.

SIDE BY SIDE THE TWO YOUNG PRINCES SPUR FORWARD ON THEIR DANGEROUS MISSION, THEIR QUARREL FORGOTTEN IN THE FACE OF ILENE'S PERIL.

AT THE BRIDGE OVER DUNDORN GLEN THEY REST AND AWAIT THE COMING OF THE RAIDERS WITH THEIR FAIR CAPTIVE.

NEXT MORNING THE RISING SUN DISCLOSES NOT ONE PARTY OF VIKINGS, BUT TWO, AND THE BRAVE LADS ARE CAUGHT BETWEEN—
NEXT WEEK- THE SINGING SWORD !

SYNOPSIS: AT DUNDORN GLEN, PRINCE VALIANT AND HIS RIVAL, STALWART PRINCE ARN, AWAIT THE BAND OF VIKING RAIDERS WHO HAVE STOLEN ILENE. AT DAWN TWO BANDS OF VIKINGS APPEAR FROM OPPOSITE DIRECTIONS AND THE BRAVE LADS ARE HEMMED IN AT THE BRIDGE.

BUT ILENE IS WITH NEITHER BAND, SO THEY MUST CUT THEIR WAY THROUGH AND CONTINUE THEIR SEARCH.

"LET'S WAIT UNTIL THAT BAND IS ON THE NARROW BRIDGE, THEN A CHARGE BETWEEN THE MOUNTED MEN WILL CAUSE GREAT CONFUSION AND MAYBE WE WILL WIN THROUGH."

"NOW BRAVE ENEMY," SHOUTS ARN, "STRIKE HARD AND TRUE FOR ENGLAND AND FAIR ILENE!"

"FOR ILENE!" RINGS THEIR BATTLE CRY AS THEY THUNDER ACROSS THE BRIDGE AND CRASH HEADLONG INTO THE CLOSE-PACKED RAIDERS!

VAL'S STRATEGY WINS THROUGH, BUT HIS HORSE, RECEIVING A MORTAL WOUND, STUMBLES AND FALLS

"GO, ARN," SAYS VAL, "THE FATE OF ILENE IS NOW IN YOUR HANDS—PURSUIT WILL BE DELAYED HERE AS LONG AS I CAN WIELD A SWORD."

ARN DRAWS HIS GREAT SWORD. "TAKE THIS, VAL, IT IS THE FAMOUS "SINGING SWORD" AND BEARS A CHARM. ONLY BY MIRACLES CAN YOU OUTLIVE THE NEXT HOUR."

70 6-12-38

HAL FOSTER

·NEXT WEEK·
THE SONG OF THE SWORD

AND ALONG THE KEEN EDGE OF THE "SINGING SWORD" THE WIND HUMS GLEEFULLY AS VAL STRIDES OUT ONTO THE BRIDGE TO FACE FIFTY ENRAGED VIKINGS!

SYNOPSIS: GLADLY WOULD PRINCE ARN HAVE STAYED TO DIE, FIGHTING SIDE BY SIDE WITH VAL, BUT THIS IS NO TIME FOR HEROIC GESTURES. ILENE IS STILL HELD BY THE VIKING RAIDERS. ARN SPURS ONWARD AND VAL PREPARES TO HOLD BACK THE PURSUIT.

"I WISH THE GODS HAD MADE YONDER BRAVE FOOL MY FRIEND INSTEAD OF MY SWORN ENEMY."

THE JEWELLED HILT OF THE "SINGING SWORD" FITS SNUGLY IN HIS HAND, AS VAL MARCHES RESOLUTELY TO HIS FATE.

THE NORTHMEN ARE BEWILDERED AT SUCH FOOLHARDY COURAGE, SUSPECTING A TRICK— BUT ONE HUGE VIKING—

A CAPTAIN, STEPS FORWARD SAYING, "MY TWO-EDGED AXE WILL SOLVE THIS RIDDLE"— VAL'S BLADE SWISHES SOFTLY, WAITING—

BUT ERE THE AXE CAN FALL, THE "SING-ING SWORD" SHRIEKS EXULTANTLY, AS THE KEEN EDGE BITES THROUGH SHIELD AND HELMET AND A WARRIOR'S SOUL GOES WINGING TO VALHALLA.

"COME CLOSER," TAUNTS VAL, "MY BEAUTIFUL SWORD IS THIRSTY," AND HALF A HUNDRED HARDY VIKINGS CROWD FORWARD.

AGAIN AND AGAIN THE TERRIBLE SWORD RISES AND FALLS, GLEAM-ING WET IN THE SUNLIGHT, AND ABOVE THE ROAR OF THE WATERS AND THE CLASHING OF ARMS CAN BE HEARD VAL'S RING-ING BATTLE-CRY, "FOR ILENE."

= NEXT WEEK =
THE EXECUTIONER

HAL FOSTER

6-19-38

SYNOPSIS: PRINCE ARN RIDES ON TO FREE THEIR BELOVED ILENE FROM THE HANDS OF RAIDERS, WHILE VAL, HIS HORSE KILLED, STANDS ALONE ON THE BRIDGE AT DUNDORN GLEN TO DELAY PURSUIT—ONE AGAINST FIFTY!

WITH RAGE IN HIS HEART AND THE TERRIBLE "SINGING SWORD" IN HIS HAND, VAL WRITES HIS NAME LARGE IN THE MEMORIES OF HIS FOES.

AT LAST THEY DRAW BACK IN AMAZEMENT AT THIS TIRELESS YOUTH WITH THE NIMBLE SWORD THAT HISSES THROUGH CHAIN AND LEATHER AND IRON.

BUT WEAKENED BY A SCORE OF WOUNDS, VAL SINKS SLOWLY TO THE GROUND, STILL FACING HIS ENEMIES.

"SURELY THIS CAN BE NO LESS THAN A KING'S SON. CARRY HIM TO OUR CHIEF TO BE RANSOMED"

WHEN VAL NEXT OPENS HIS EYES HE IS BEING BORNE TO THE COAST ON THE WARRIORS' SPEARS—WELL, HIS WORK IS DONE; ARN HAS ESCAPED TO FIND ILENE.

BESIDE HIS TWO SHIPS SITS THAGNAR, THE SEA ROVER, AWAITING THE RETURN OF HIS RAIDERS. WHEN VAL IS BROUGHT BEFORE HIM HE ROARS, "I TOLD YOU MEN NOT TO ANNOY ME WITH PRISONERS."

"KILL HIM," ORDERS THAGNAR. HE SPOKE THE SAME LANGUAGE AS VAL'S FATHER, THE EXILED KING.

72 6-26-38

"NOW, IF I WISHED TO KILL A MAN I'D DO IT, MYSELF," MOCKS VAL, "BUT PERHAPS BOLD THAGNAR PREFERS TO REST IN THE SHADE LIKE AN OLD WOMAN AND HAS NO TASTE FOR DANGER."

"THE BANTAM COCK CROWS LOUD.—YES, THAGNAR WILL REST IN THE SHADE WHILE YOU MAKE GOOD YOUR BOAST AGAINST MY EXECUTIONER WHO SITS YONDER, WHETTING HIS DEADLY BLADE."

HAL FOSTER

NEXT WEEK—"A PLEA FOR MERCY"

SYNOPSIS: MISTRESS ILENE AND HER TWO PRINCELY LOVERS ARE CAUGHT IN A VIKING RAID, BUT VAL'S BLOODY DEED WITH THE SINGING SWORD ENABLES ARN TO ESCAPE AND SEEK MEANS FOR THEIR RESCUE. THAGNAR ORDERS HIS MEN TO KILL VAL, BUT HE SO TAUNTS THE VIKING CHIEFTAIN THAT —

"SO—OUR LITTLE ROOSTER STILL WANTS TO FIGHT, EH? THEN HE MAY AMUSE US BY DANCING WITH OUR EXECUTIONER."

DROOPING WITH WEARINESS AND WEAKENED BY A SCORE OF WOUNDS, VAL FACES HIS TREMENDOUS OPPONENT.

THE MIGHTY EXECUTIONER TOYS WITH HIM SAYING, "I SHALL INFLICT A THOUSAND SMALL WOUNDS UNTIL YOU HOWL FOR MERCY."

"NAY," SAYS VAL LOUD ENOUGH FOR ALL TO HEAR, "FOR I SEE BY THE STUPIDITY ON YOUR DULL FACE THAT YOU WILL FALL A VICTIM—

TO ANY SIMPLE TRICK AND WILL HOWL TO ME FOR MERCY—

WHEN YOUR BONES CRACKLE LIKE DRY TWIGS!"

CLAMPING A TERRIBLE GRIP ON THE BEWILDERED GIANT, VAL EXERTS ALL HIS REMAINING STRENGTH—

7-3-38

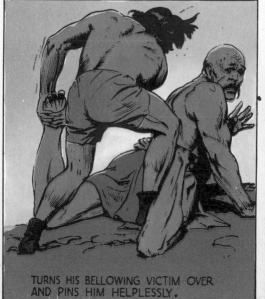

TURNS HIS BELLOWING VICTIM OVER AND PINS HIM HELPLESSLY.

HAL FOSTER

"SHALL I LEAN FORWARD AND MAIM YOUR EXECUTIONER, THAGNAR, OR ARE YOU SATISFIED?"

NEXT WEEK—ILENE!

SYNOPSIS: VAL, A PRISONER OF THE VIKINGS, IS CONDEMNED TO DEATH, BUT HE TRICKS THAGNAR INTO LETTING HIM DIE FIGHTING AND THEN TRICKS HIS HUGE OPPONENT INTO HELPLESSNESS.

"WHAT DOES THAGNAR SAY NOW?" "ENOUGH,— YOU HAVE WELL-EARNED YOUR FREEDOM—YOU MAY GO."

"IT IS NOT FREE-DOM FOR MYSELF I DESIRE, BUT FOR ANOTHER WHOM YOUR RAIDERS HAVE TAKEN-

"YONDER MAID, ILENE OF BRANWYN, FOR WHOM I HAVE BEEN SEARCHING."

FOR VAL'S QUICK EYE HAD SEEN A BAND OF RETURNING RAIDERS WITH GOLDEN-HAIRED ILENE AMONG THEIR LOOT.

"WHAT," ROARS THAGNAR, "WAS IT FOR THIS THIN WENCH YOU RISKED YOUR LIFE, KILLED MY MEN AND RUINED MY EXECUTIONER?"

BUT VAL HAS ALREADY FOR-GOTTEN SUCH TRIVIAL TROUBLES AS THAGNAR AND HIS VIKINGS IN THE JOY OF SEEING ILENE AGAIN.

"HAVE COURAGE; ARN IS FREE AND WILL, SOMEHOW, CONTRIVE OUR RESCUE — AND YOU ARE LOVELIER THAN EVER!"

7-10-38

"I MUST HAVE THIS LAD, HE HAS WIT AND DARING, COURAGE AND SKILL. HE WILL CAPTAIN ONE OF MY SHIPS AND BE-COME A GREAT SEA-ROVER."

THE TWO DESPERATE YOUNG LOVERS ARE PLACED UNDER GUARD UNTIL THE SHIPS ARE MADE READY.

THAGNAR MUST HAVE COME FROM THE EAST WHERE ONCE VAL'S FATHER HAD RULED, FOR HE SPEAKS THE SAME TONGUE — VAL SCRATCHES A MESSAGE ON A ROCK.

FOR VAL KNOWS THAT PRINCE ARN WILL NEVER FALTER IN A QUEST ONCE UNDERTAKEN AND, SOONER OR LATER, WILL FIND HIS MESSAGE —NOR IS HE WRONG!

HAL FOSTER

NEXT WEEK: THE PURSUIT

SYNOPSIS: VAL AND PRINCE ARN ARE BATTLING FOR THE HAND OF ILENE. WHEN ALL THREE ARE CAUGHT IN A VIKING RAID. VAL'S GOOD USE OF THE SINGING SWORD ALLOWS ARN TO ESCAPE AND HE SEARCHES FRANTICALLY FOR ILENE.

ILENE— EAST TO LITES LAND

FOLLOWING THE RAIDERS TO THE COAST, HE ARRIVES TOO LATE AND FINDS ONLY VAL'S MESSAGE SCRATCHED ON A STONE.

CASTING ASIDE HIS HEAVY ARMOR, ARN RACES MADLY TO HIS FATHER'S PALACE AT ORD.

AFTER BITTER ARGUING THE KING AT LAST CONSENTS TO FURNISH A SHIP AND MEN FOR THE PURSUIT.

A PICKED COMPANY OF SAILORS AND ADVENTUROUS YOUNG KNIGHTS AWAIT IMPATIENTLY THE INCOMING TIDE.

7-17-38

WISHING TO WIN VAL OVER TO HIS BAND, THAGNAR SHOWS HIS PRISONERS EVERY COURTESY—WHILE HE LOVINGLY HOLDS THE BEAUTIFUL, DEADLY SINGING SWORD.

"BE CALM, ILENE—FAR ASTERN I SEE A PURSUING SAIL. BRAVE ARN IS COMING."

TO GIVE ARN TIME TO APPROACH UNSEEN THEY DIRECT ATTENTION FORWARD.

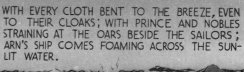

WITH EVERY CLOTH BENT TO THE BREEZE, EVEN TO THEIR CLOAKS; WITH PRINCE AND NOBLES STRAINING AT THE OARS BESIDE THE SAILORS; ARN'S SHIP COMES FOAMING ACROSS THE SUN-LIT WATER.

NEXT WEEK—A SIREN SONG

SYNOPSIS: SATISFIED WITH HIS LOOT AND PRISONERS, THAGNAR SETS SAIL FOR HOME. VAL AND ILENE, GAZING LONGINGLY AT THE FADING SHORES OF ENGLAND, SEE A PURSUING SAIL ON THE FAR HORIZON.

IT IS PRINCE ARN IN SWIFT PURSUIT, SAILS SET AND EVERY MAN STRAINING AT THE OARS.

ARN'S SHIP GAINS RAPIDLY AND IS SOON IN PLAIN SIGHT—IF ONLY VAL CAN HOLD THE SEA-ROVERS' ATTENTION UNTIL ARN IS WITHIN STRIKING DISTANCE!

SEIZING A LYRE FROM AMONG THE PILE OF LOOT, VAL RUNS FORWARD AND LEAPS INTO THE SHROUDS.

LIFTING HIS CLEAR VOICE IN A WILD, HAUNTING MELODY, HE SINGS OF HIS HOME IN THE LONELY MARSHES WHERE THE SEA-WIND FOREVER WHISPERS AN ANCIENT SONG AMONG THE SWAYING REEDS. THE FIERCE SEA-ROVERS RELAX AND DREAM OF THEIR LITTLE HOMES BESIDE THE RESTLESS SEA.

AND CLOSER AND YET CLOSER GLIDES ARN'S SHIP, UNNOTICED UNTIL THE BEAT OF THE OARS CAN BE PLAINLY HEARD.

THEN THE PIRATES AWAKE WITH A START AND ORDERS ARE SHOUTED BY THE ANGRY THAGNAR.

THE SECOND SHIP SHORTENS SAIL AND TURNS TO INTERCEPT THE DARING PURSUERS.

NEXT WEEK - THE SEA FIGHT

In the Service of King Arthur

VAL HOLDS THE SEA-ROVER'S ATTENTION UNTIL PRINCE ARN'S RESCUE SHIP IS ALMOST UPON THEM. ONE OF THE TWO PIRATE SHIPS TURNS TO INTERCEPT.

THE SEA-ROVER SHORTENS SAIL AND PREPARES FOR BATTLE.

SWINGING WIDE MOMENTARILY ARN SUDDENLY TURNS AND BEARS DOWN ON HIS ENEMY.

DRIVEN BY SAIL AND OAR ENGLISH OAK MEETS DANISH CEDAR WITH A TEARING CRASH.

BUT A SEA FIGHT IS THE BREATH OF LIFE TO THESE HARDY ROVERS AND THEY SWARM UPON ARN'S SHIP.

AND THAGNAR SAILS CALMLY ON WITH ALL THE TREASURES FROM HIS RAIDS — THERE WILL NOW BE LESS TO DIVIDE IT AMONG.

VAL IS DESPERATE! STRIKING THAGNAR A STAGGERING BLOW HE TEARS THE "SINGING SWORD" FROM HIS GRASP —

SPEEDS TO THE MAST AND BRINGS THE GREAT SAIL CRASHING DOWN AMONG THE ASTONISHED VIKINGS.

AVOIDING HIS PURSUERS, HE RUNS NIMBLY AFT ON THE GUNWALE —

7-31-38

STRIKES DOWN THE HELMSMAN AND, BEFORE ANYONE CAN REACH HIM, CRIPPLES THE STEERING SWEEP.

HAL FOSTER

NEXT WEEK—ILENE ALONE

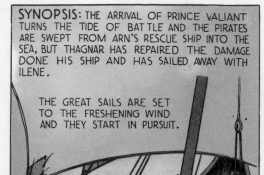

SYNOPSIS: THE ARRIVAL OF PRINCE VALIANT TURNS THE TIDE OF BATTLE AND THE PIRATES ARE SWEPT FROM ARN'S RESCUE SHIP INTO THE SEA, BUT THAGNAR HAS REPAIRED THE DAMAGE DONE HIS SHIP AND HAS SAILED AWAY WITH ILENE.

THE GREAT SAILS ARE SET TO THE FRESHENING WIND AND THEY START IN PURSUIT.

AT SUNSET THE WIND HAS BECOME A HOWLING GALE, BUT STILL ARN HOLDS HIS COURSE.

WHEN THE FULL FORCE OF THE STORM BURSTS UPON THEM, THEY WORK LIKE MAD TO KEEP THE CRAFT AFLOAT.

THROUGH THE NIGHT THEY RIDE THE MOUNTAINOUS WAVES AT A SEA-ANCHOR.

AT DAWN THERE IS NO SIGN OF THAGNAR'S SHIP IN ALL THAT EMPTY WASTE OF ANGRY SEA.

THEN BEGINS THE LONG, WEARY SEARCH FOR SOME NEWS OF THAGNAR—FROM THE GRIM FIORDS OF THE NORTH TO THE SALT MARSHES IN THE SOUTH.

WEARIED FROM ALMOST CONSTANT FIGHTING THE TATTERED SURVIVORS AT LAST CALL A HALT.

"GALLANT COMPANIONS, THE SEARCH BY SEA IS FRUITLESS, SO VAL AND I WILL CONTINUE ON LAND, ALONE. GOOD-BYE AND GOOD LUCK."

THE SHIP DEPARTS AND THE TWO RIVALS FACE A STRANGE CONTINENT ALONE.

NEXT WEEK — THE SEARCH

SYNOPSIS: DAY AFTER DAY THEY SEARCH THE EMPTY SEA FOR THAGNAR'S SHIP — THE SHIP THAT CARRIED AWAY LOVELY ILENE. DISMISSING THEIR OWN VESSEL, ARN AND VAL SET OUT BY LAND TO SEEK THAGNAR'S VILLAGE.

THE YOUNG PRINCES BID FAREWELL TO THE LAST LINK WITH THEIR HOMELAND.

ACROSS WEARY MILES OF SHIFTING SANDS THEY MARCH SIDE BY SIDE.

AT EVERY HUT AND VILLAGE THEY INQUIRE OF THAGNAR'S WHEREABOUTS, ALWAYS IN DANGER.

WEEK AFTER WEEK IN SUN AND STORM, NEVER FALTERING, ACROSS THE GREAT SALT MARSHES —

AND IN THE DEPTHS OF GREAT FORESTS THEY SEARCH FOR SOME HINT THAT WILL LEAD THEM TO ILENE.

DESPITE THEIR HARDSHIPS AND DANGERS, THEY PRACTISE THE RULES OF COURTESY AND FORTITUDE LAID DOWN BY THEIR WISE KING ARTHUR —

AND EACH DAY SET ASIDE AN HOUR TO BETTER THEMSELVES AT SWORD PLAY.

AT LAST THEY MEET SOME FISHERMEN WHO SPEAK THE SAME LANGUAGE AS THAGNAR DOES. THEY ADVISE THE BOYS TO SEEK THAGNAR'S KING FOR INFORMATION.

"KING SLIGON OF THULE! THE TYRANT WHO STOLE MY FATHER'S THRONE AND I MUST BEG HIM FOR A FAVOR!" SAYS VAL BITTERLY, "OR BE MURDERED IF YOU ARE RECOGNIZED," ADDS ARN.

TURNING INLAND AS DIRECTED, THEY AT LAST COME IN SIGHT OF THE KING'S CASTLE.

"ONCE MY FATHER DEALT JUSTICE IN YONDER CASTLE WHERE NOW A TYRANT RULES AND WEEDS GROW IN THE GARDENS WHERE I PLAYED IN CHILDHOOD."

8-21-38

AND AGAIN PRINCE VALIANT ENTERS THE FAMILIAR PORTALS THAT HE ONCE CALLED HOME.
NEXT WEEK — THE TYRANT

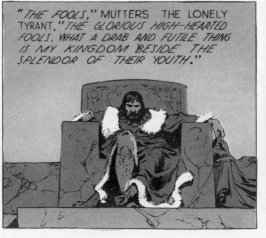

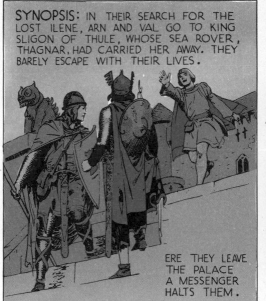

SYNOPSIS: IN THEIR SEARCH FOR THE LOST ILENE, ARN AND VAL GO TO KING SLIGON OF THULE, WHOSE SEA ROVER, THAGNAR, HAD CARRIED HER AWAY. THEY BARELY ESCAPE WITH THEIR LIVES.

ERE THEY LEAVE THE PALACE A MESSENGER HALTS THEM.

"THE KING BIDS YOU TAKE YONDER BOAT AND GO TO THE MOUTH OF THE RIVER, WHERE YOU WILL FIND THAGNAR'S VILLAGE."

SWIFTLY THEY GLIDE DOWNSTREAM FOLLOWING THEIR FIRST REAL CLUE.

THE VILLAGERS TELL THEM:—*"THAGNAR NEVER RETURNED FROM HIS RAID ON THE ENGLISH COAST."*

WITH DESPAIR IN THEIR HEARTS THEY SEARCH THE SHORE, MOVING EVER WESTWARD.

ONE DAY THEY SEE THE BLEACHING RIBS OF A WRECKED SHIP WHICH THEY RECOGNIZE AS THAGNAR'S.

AND AMID THE WRECKAGE FIND BOLD THAGNAR'S HORNED HELMET.

Copr. 1938, King Features Syndicate, Inc., World rights reserved

9-4-38 FURTHER DIGGING REVEALS THAT WHICH THEY FEARED MOST TO FIND, A JEWELED CLASP,—ILENE'S !

TWO DESPERATELY UNHAPPY LADS FACE A WORLD NO LONGER MADE GAY BY THE BRIGHT HAIR AND LAUGHING EYES OF THE MAID THEY HAD LOVED. •*NEXT WEEK—HOMEWARD.*•

HAL FOSTER

SYNOPSIS
ILENE OF THE HONEY-COLORED HAIR HAD GONE AND WITH HER ALL THE JOY AND HAPPINESS HER TWO PRINCELY LOVERS HAD KNOWN. THEY HAD FACED DEATH AND DANGER WITH A LAUGH, HARDSHIP WITH A SHRUG, BUT THE ENDING OF ALL THEIR DREAMS LEAVES THEM HEARTBROKEN AND BEWILDERED IN A LONELY WORLD

ON A LEDGE ABOVE THE WRECKED SHIP THEY BUILD A CAIRN TO THE MEMORY OF THE FAIR ILENE.

SILENTLY THEY TURN WESTWARD TO SEEK SOME WAY OF CROSSING THE ROUGH SEA THAT SEPARATES THEM FROM ENGLAND.

ONE STORMY DAY A WIDE RIVER-MOUTH BARS THEIR WAY

WHILE GATHERING DRIFTWOOD FOR A RAFT VAL SUDDENLY SHOUTS, "LOOK, A GREAT SHIP IS BEING DRIVEN TO DESTRUCTION BY THE WAVES."

"BUILD A SIGNAL FIRE TO ATTRACT THEIR ATTENTION, ARN, WHILE I SWIM ACROSS TO THE OTHER POINT."

THE MARINERS SEE THEIR SIGNAL AND THE TWO BOYS GUIDE THE PITCHING VESSEL INTO THE SAFETY OF THE RIVER-MOUTH.

"LOOK, ARN, KNIGHTS OF THE ROUND TABLE, SIR KAY, PERCIVAL, NEGARTH, TRISTRAM AND VRIENS. WE ARE SAVED!"

·NEXT WEEK·
HOMEWARD BOUND

HAL FOSTER

9-11-38

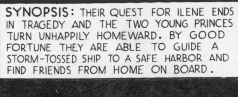

SYNOPSIS: THEIR QUEST FOR ILENE ENDS IN TRAGEDY AND THE TWO YOUNG PRINCES TURN UNHAPPILY HOMEWARD. BY GOOD FORTUNE THEY ARE ABLE TO GUIDE A STORM-TOSSED SHIP TO A SAFE HARBOR AND FIND FRIENDS FROM HOME ON BOARD.

THE GREAT SHIP COMES ROCKING IN FROM THE SEA AND DROPS ANCHOR.

A BOAT IS SENT ASHORE TO FETCH THE RESCUERS ABOARD

AND A WHOLEHEARTED WELCOME IS GIVEN THE TWO HAGGARD WANDERERS.

THE ONCE GAY AND WITTY VAL TELLS OF THEIR FRANTIC QUEST, ITS PITIFUL END AND THE WEARY RETURN.

"THE GLAD TIDINGS WE BRING MAY EASE YOUR SORROW," SAYS KINDLY SIR ECTOR, "FOR KING ARTHUR HAS DRIVEN THE ANGLES TO THE COAST AND MADE ENGLAND SAFE AGAIN."

"AND WE GO TO FETCH THE NOBLE SIR LAUNCELOT OUT OF BRITTANY TO ATTEND THE GREATEST TOURNAMENT IN HISTORY IN CELEBRATION OF THE VICTORY."

WHEN THE STORM ABATES THE GAY COMPANY SAILS UP THE COAST OF GAUL AND BRITTANY.

AND ENTERS THE HARBOR BENEATH THE FROWNING CASTLE OF KING BORS AND HIS SON, SIR LAUNCELOT.

9-18-38

BUT VAL AND ARN HAVE NO HEART FOR THE GAIETY WITHIN THE CASTLE THAT NIGHT.

NEXT WEEK — LAUNCELOT'S COUNSEL

HAL FOSTER

SYNOPSIS: TOGETHER PRINCE ARN AND VAL HAVE SEARCHED WILD NORTHERN SEAS AND HOSTILE COASTS FOR NEWS OF ILENE, ONLY TO LEARN IN THE END THAT THEIR BELOVED HAS PERISHED IN A STORM. IN THE QUIET GARDENS SIR LAUNCELOT FINDS THE TWO DESPERATELY UNHAPPY LADS.

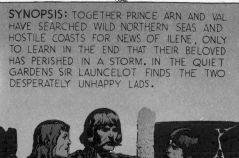

"DO NOT GRIEVE FOR ILENE — FATE HAS SPARED HER MUCH UNHAPPINESS."

"HAD SHE BEEN FOUND YOU WERE PLEDGED TO FIGHT TO THE DEATH FOR HER HAND'; THE WINNER WOULD LIVE ON KNOWING HE HAD BOUGHT A BRIDE WITH HIS FRIEND'S LIFE, AND GENTLE ILENE WOULD BE THE WIFE OF A MURDERER, FOREVER BLAMING HERSELF FOR BEING THE CAUSE OF IT ALL."

"SIR LAUNCELOT IS RIGHT, ARN, AND OUR QUEST MIGHT HAVE ENDED EVEN MORE DISASTROUSLY."

AT DAWN THE STATELY WAR-SHIP LEAVES FOR ENGLAND AND THE GREAT TOURNAMENT.

SAILING UP THE SOLENT THEY LAND AND JOIN THE MARCH TO CAMELOT, A GAY LAUGHING TROOP.

"HERE I MUST LEAVE FOR MY FATHER'S KINGDOM AT ORD, BUT IN YOUR CARE I LEAVE THE CHARMED SINGING SWORD TO BE USED IN GOOD KING ARTHUR'S CAUSE."

9-25-38

MANY KNIGHTS THRONG THE ROADS UNTIL A SPLENDID PROCESSION WITH BANNERS FLYING AND TRUMPETS SOUNDING, MOVES ON TO CAMELOT, CITY OF WONDER.   · NEXT WEEK — KING ARTHUR ·

BOISTEROUSLY GAY SIR GAWAIN WELCOMES HIS WANDERING SQUIRE!

PRINCE VALIANT IS HONORED BY THE KING'S INTEREST AND HE TELLS ARTHUR AND GUINEVERE OF HIS TRAGIC QUEST.

"AND NOW, SIRE," IMPLORES VAL, "GRANT ME SOME GREAT QUEST WHOSE FULFILLMENT WILL MAKE ME WORTHY OF KNIGHTHOOD, FOR I CRAVE FELLOWSHIP OF THE ROUND TABLE ABOVE ALL ELSE."

"YOU ARE BUT A LAD YET, PRINCE VALIANT," SAYS KING ARTHUR, "WHEN YOU HAVE GROWN STRONG ENOUGH TO CONTEND ON EQUAL TERMS WITH MY VETERAN KNIGHTS, — PERHAPS."

"PERHAPS IF I SPILL SOME OF HIS BEST KNIGHTS AT THE TOURNAMENT THE KING WILL TAKE NOTICE."

MIDNIGHT IN THE DESERTED ARMORY AND VAL GATHERS AND REPAIRS BITS OF ABANDONED ARMOR.

AND PAINTS ALL WHITE HIS ASSEMBLED ARMS — SIGN OF AN UNTRIED KNIGHT.

86 10-2-38

WHEN THE SPLENDID CONCOURSE OF KNIGHTS, THEIR LADIES AND RETAINERS LEAVE FOR CAERLEON AND THE GREAT TOURNAMENT, THE SILENT WHITE KNIGHT RIDES WITH THEM IN SECOND-HAND ARMOR, ON A BORROWED CHARGER.

HAL FOSTER

SYNOPSIS: KING ARTHUR HAS HINTED THAT VAL IS TOO YOUNG TO CONTEND WITH VETERAN KNIGHTS. BUT, WITH THE CONFIDENCE OF YOUTH, VAL IN A SECOND HAND SUIT OF ARMOR ENTERS THE GREAT TOURNAMENT TO TRY FOR HIS GOLDEN SPURS.

VAL WAITS ALONE AND UNATTENDED FOR HE DARE NOT TRUST HIS FELLOW SQUIRES OR MEN-AT-ARMS, WHO ARE ENVIOUS OF HIS PRINCELY BEARING AND POPULARITY WITH THE KNIGHTS OF THE ROUND TABLE.

TRUMPETS SOUND AND A MIGHTY SHOUT GOES UP AS TWO HUNDRED BRILLIANT KNIGHTS SWING INTO THEIR SADDLES.

THEY FACE EACH OTHER IN TWO LONG LINES— KING ARTHUR GIVES THE SIGNAL—

THE EARTH SHAKES WITH THE THUNDER OF HOOFS AND THE FIRST FLIGHT CRASHES TO VICTORY OR DEFEAT.

IT IS ROUGH AND DANGEROUS SPORT AND AT THE END OF THE FOURTH FLIGHT BUT TEN KNIGHTS ARE LEFT FOR THE CHALLENGE ROUND.

THESE TEN MAY CHALLENGE WHOM THEY PLEASE TO SINGLE COMBAT—TO THE ASTONISHMENT OF ALL THE WHITE KNIGHT TURNS TO THE PARK OF CHAMPIONS

AND STRIKES THE SHIELD OF TRISTRAM, GREATEST OF ALL WARRIORS SAVE ONLY LAUNCELOT, A CHALLENGE HAS BEEN GIVEN !

10-9-38

NEXT WEEK—
A LONG CHANCE

SYNOPSIS: IN SECOND-HAND ARMOR AND ON A BORROWED HORSE, VAL ENTERS THE GREAT TOURNAMENT DETERMINED TO WIN HIS GOLDEN SPURS. FROM THE GRAND MELEE HE EMERGES ONE OF THE VICTORS — IMMEDIATELY HE CHALLENGES MIGHTY TRISTRAM TO SINGLE COMBAT.

THE NEXT FEW MINUTES WILL BRING VAL EITHER CRUSHING DEFEAT OR A CHANCE FOR KNIGHTHOOD.

"THIS UNKNOWN WHITE KNIGHT HAS MORE COURAGE THAN SENSE — FIND OUT WHO HE IS AND WHETHER HE WIN OR LOSE, BRING HIM HERE TO ME," SAYS THE KING.

THE TRICK OF THE SLANTING SHIELD DEFLECTS TRISTRAM'S LANCE AS HIS OWN IS SHATTERED BY THE IMPACT.

THERE IS AN EMBARRASSING PAUSE THEN A RIPPLE OF LAUGHTER FROM THE CROWD WHEN THEY REALIZE THE UNKNOWN KNIGHT OWNS BUT ONE LANCE.

10-16-38

BUT SIR GAWAIN HAS RIGHTLY GUESSED WHO THE WHITE KNIGHT REALLY IS — "HONOR ME BY USING MINE," HE SAYS, THEN WHISPERS, "YOU STOUT-HEARTED YOUNG IDIOT."

TRISTRAM IS NO LONGER SMILING. "BRING ME MY STOUTEST LANCE," HE ORDERS, "THIS NAMELESS UPSTART STRIKES LIKE A THUNDER-BOLT."

HAL FOSTER

TRUMPETS SOUND AND AGAIN THE SIGNAL IS GIVEN! —
NEXT WEEK — LOUD LAUGHTER

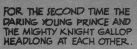

FOR THE SECOND TIME THE DARING YOUNG PRINCE AND THE MIGHTY KNIGHT GALLOP HEADLONG AT EACH OTHER.

TRISTRAM IS WELL-NIGH LIFTED FROM HIS SADDLE ERE VAL'S WEAPON SPLINTERS — HIS OWN STOUT LANCE HOLDS AND VAL AND HIS HORSE GO CRASHING TO DEFEAT.

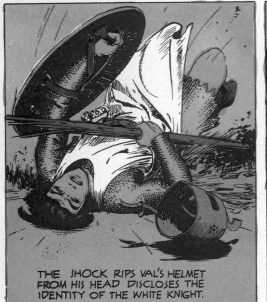

THE SHOCK RIPS VAL'S HELMET FROM HIS HEAD DISCLOSES THE IDENTITY OF THE WHITE KNIGHT.

LOUD JEERS RING OUT FROM HIS FELLOW SQUIRES AS VAL IS RECOGNIZED, FOR THEY ARE ENVIOUS OF HIS POPULARITY WITH THE KNIGHTS.

DAZEDLY VAL WALKS FROM THE FIELD AMID A THUNDER OF APPLAUSE.

"MAY I NEVER HAVE TO MEET THAT YOUNG SPITFIRE AGAIN" SAYS TRISTRAM, "I ACHE ALL OVER FROM HIS BLOWS."

"WHY, IT WAS YOUNG PRINCE VALIANT WHO WELL-NIGH UNSEATED THE MIGHTY TRISTRAM," EXCLAIMS THE KING. "BRING HIM TO ME."

BUT HAL HEARD ONLY THE JEERS OF THE SQUIRES AND THINKS THE WHOLE ENSEMBLAGE IS LAUGHING AT HIS PRESUMPTION. QUIETLY HE LEAVES CAERLEON.

HAL FOSTER

SYNOPSIS: THE MIGHTY TRISTRAM AT LAST TUMBLES VAL FROM HIS HORSE. AS HE LIMPS FROM THE FIELD GREAT CHEERS RING OUT FOR HIS GALLANT EFFORT, BUT VAL HEARS THE JEERS OF THE ENVIOUS SQUIRES AND THINKS THE WHOLE CROWD MOCKS HIM. QUIETLY, HE RETURNS TO CAMELOT.

THE YOUNG PRINCE IS DEEPLY HURT BY THE FANCIED MOCKERY.

AS FIRST HE CAME TO CAMELOT SO NOW DOES HE LEAVE, RICHER ONLY BY HIS POSSESSION OF THE SINGING SWORD.

AND HE TURNS HIS STEPS TOWARD THE PEACE AND QUIET OF HIS OLD HOME IN THE MYSTERIOUS FENS.

BY THE EDGE OF THE GREAT MARSH HE MEETS AGAIN HIS BOYHOOD FRIEND.

THE YOUNG SHEPHERD AGREES TO TAKE CARE OF VAL'S MOUNTS.

TO HIS GREAT JOY, VAL FINDS HIS OLD DUGOUT STILL IN ITS HIDING-PLACE.

WITH MELTED RESIN AND CHARCOAL HE REPAIRS THE CRACKS

ONCE AGAIN HE DRIVES HIS SLENDER CANOE SWIFTLY THROUGH THE MAZE OF CHANNELS,-HIS SPIRITS RISING IN THE FREEDOM OF THE FAMILIAR SWAMPS.

HAL FOSTER

AFTER TWO YEARS OF WANDERING, VAL ONCE MORE APPROACHES THE ISLAND WHER HIS KINGLY FATHER LIVES IN EXILE.

WHILE AT COURT THE KING COMMANDS "BRING ME PRINCE VALIANT THAT HE MAY BE KNIGHTED -- STRONGER WARRIORS THERE MAY BE, BUT NONE MORE BRAVE OR SKILLFUL!"

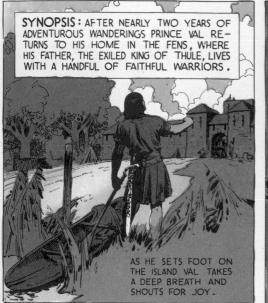

SYNOPSIS: AFTER NEARLY TWO YEARS OF ADVENTUROUS WANDERINGS PRINCE VAL RETURNS TO HIS HOME IN THE FENS, WHERE HIS FATHER, THE EXILED KING OF THULE, LIVES WITH A HANDFUL OF FAITHFUL WARRIORS.

AS HE SETS FOOT ON THE ISLAND VAL TAKES A DEEP BREATH AND SHOUTS FOR JOY.

FROM THE GATEWAY COMES AN ANSWERING SHOUT — "PRINCE VALIANT HAS RETURNED TO US! WELCOME, VAL."

AND THE AGING VETERANS CROWD AROUND THE STALWART YOUNG WARRIOR WHO HAD LEFT THEM AS A BOY.

SHOUTING LUSTILY THEY HURRY TO THE LOW RAFTERED HALL WHERE THE KING, HIS FACE BEAMING WITH PLEASURE, RISES TO WELCOME HIS DARING SON.

BEFORE THE GREAT FIREPLACE VAL RECOUNTS HIS STORY TO THE KING.

ONCE MORE THE HUNTER, VAL ROAMS FAR AND FREE ACROSS HIS BELOVED FENS.

THE OLD FASCINATION OF THE GREAT WASTE COMES BACK AND HOLDS HIM — FOR A WHILE HE IS CONTENT.

11-6-38

BUT, AFTER THE CLASH OF BATTLES AND THE HIGH ADVENTURINGS OF KING ARTHUR'S COURT, THIS IS BUT CHILD'S PLAY. WHILE WINTER WINDS HOWL MOURNFULLY AROUND THE HOUSE VAL LAYS GREAT PLANS FOR THE FUTURE.

•NEXT WEEK•
AGAIN THE WITCH!

HAL FOSTER

SYNOPSIS: WHEN HE TOLD HIS FATHER THE STORY OF HIS ADVENTURES VAL DID NOT TELL THE EXILED KING OF HIS MEETING WITH SLIGON, THE TYRANT WHO HAD USURPED THE THRONE OF THULE— NOW HE PLANS TO REGAIN THE LOST KINGDOM AND FREE THE PEOPLE FROM OPPRESSION. WITH THIRTY AGING WAR— RIORS HE WOULD CONQUER AN ARMY!

FAR OFF IN THE HEART OF THE FENS LIVES HORRIT, THE WITCH WHO HAD PROPHESIED ALL TOO TRULY THE TRAGEDIES OF VAL'S LIFE. TO HER VAL WOULD GO AGAIN FOR COUNSEL.

WHEN BITTER JANUARY WINDS HOLD TIGHT THE GREAT SWAMP IN AN ICY GRIP VAL SPEEDS ON HIS MISSION

FANTASTIC NORTHERN LIGHTS DANCE WEIRDLY ACROSS THE STILL NIGHT AS HE REACHES THE BLEAK HOVEL.

HORRIT AND HER HIDEOUS SON SCREAM IN TERROR AT VAL'S UNEXPECTED INTRUSION.

"I BRING FOOD AND A WARM CLOAK AS GIFTS, NOW TELL ME WHAT A MAN MAY ACCOMPLISH WITH THE SINGING SWORD?"

"HIDE THAT ACCURSED BLADE FROM MY SIGHT," WAILS THE WITCH, "THAT IS THE CHARMED SWORD, FLAMBERGE, MADE BY THE SAME MAGE WHO FORGED KING ARTHUR'S EXCALIBUR!"

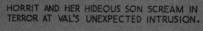

"NO KEENER BLADE WAS EVER WROUGHT AND TO ITS OWNER WILL COME HARD VICTORY, IF HE FIGHT WITH A PURE HEART AND IN A GOOD CAUSE, BUT WOE TO HIM WHO USES IT FOR EVIL GAIN! GET RID OF IT, PRETTY BOY, FOR IT IS A TERRIBLE MASTER!" THEN SHE PROPHESIES WHAT MAY NOT BE TOLD HERE, BUT VAL IS WHITE AND TREMBLING WHEN—

11-13-38

HAL FOSTER

HE EMERGES INTO THE THIN, COLD DAWN AND FLEES HOMEWARD, SHIVERING WITH DREAD—
NEXT WEEK — THIN ICE

SYNOPSIS: VAL HAD CROSSED ON THE ICE TO HEAR THE TERRIBLE PROPHECY OF HORRIT, THE WITCH. TREMBLING WITH HORROR HE STARTS HOMEWARD IN THE DAWN. THE SUN RISES CLEAR AND STRONG AND THE SNOW MELTS RAPIDLY.

VAL BECOMES UNEASY AND BREAKS INTO A SWIFT RUN.

UNDER THE CLOUDLESS SKY THE ICE BECOMES DESPERATELY THIN AND CRACKS UNDER EVERY FOOTFALL. FOR THE FIRST TIME VAL KNOWS WHAT FEAR IS!

HOUR AFTER HOUR OF EXHAUSTING EFFORT ONLY TO CRASH THROUGH AT LAST!

TOO THIN TO BEAR HIS WEIGHT, TOO THICK TO SWIM AGAINST —— FAR AWAY SOME DEAD TREES SIGNIFY LAND.

TOWARD THEM VAL SWIMS UNDER THE ICE, HIS TIRED BODY NUMBED BY THE CHILL WATER.

OCCASIONALLY HE CROUCHES ON THE BOTTOM AND SPRINGS UPWARD, CRASHING THROUGH FOR A BREATH OF AIR.

TWO OF THE DEAD TREES ARE STILL FIRM, WEARILY HE TRIMS ONE SIDE SMOOTH.

AT SUNSET A COLD WIND STRENGTHENS THE ICE AND FREEZES THE WET CLOTHES TO HIS SHIVERING BODY.

11-20-38

MIDNIGHT —— AND A WAKEFUL GUARD HEARS A SOUND AT THE OUTER DOOR ——

NEXT WEEK — VISIONS

THEY FIND HIM HALF-CONSCIOUS AT THE OUTER GATE AND HELP HIM INTO THE WARM KITCHEN.

THE SOLDIERS BUILD A GREAT FIRE, WRAP HIM IN WARM CLOAKS AND REVIVE HIM WITH A HOT DRINK.

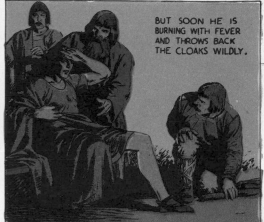

BUT SOON HE IS BURNING WITH FEVER AND THROWS BACK THE CLOAKS WILDLY.

THE SOLDIERS BECOME WORRIED AND PUT HIM TO BED WHERE HE TOSSES FEVERISHLY.

THEN FOLLOWS ANXIOUS DAYS WHEN THE GRIZZLED VETERANS STAND OUTSIDE HIS DOOR IN SILENT MISERY, WHILE VAL BATTLES FOR EVERY BREATH.

THE LONELY KING KEEPS LONG VIGIL. HIS KINGDOM HAS BEEN STOLEN, HIS STATELY QUEEN HAS PASSED AWAY AND NOW HIS ONLY SON IS FIGHTING WEAKLY FOR HIS LIFE WITH THE GRIM OPPONENT.

IN DELIRIUM VAL LIVES AGAIN THE CROWDED, ZESTFUL DAYS OF HIS SERVICE UNDER KING ARTHUR, WHEN HE RODE AT ADVENTURE TO FAR, STRANGE PLACES; AGAIN HE SEES THE GREAT SEA CROCODILE, BALDON'S STUPID, CRUEL FROWN; BOLD THAGNAR AND HIS MIGHTY EXECUTIONER, THE GREAT KING AND MERRY GAWAIN, BEAUTIFUL, EVIL MORGAN LE FEY AND THE OGRE OF SINSTAR WOOD AND AGAIN HE FOUGHT PRINCE ARN WHILE THE NOON SUN SLID DOWN THE WESTERN SKY,— IRON TRISTRAM'S CHARGE, COURTEOUS LAUNCELOT AND WISE MERLIN; HIS MOTHER'S STILL FACE AND EVER HOVERING NEAR; GENTLE ILENE.

HAL FOSTER

NEXT WEEK — *THE GREAT PLAN*

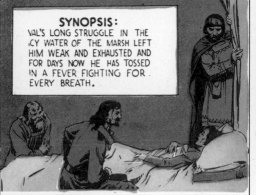

SYNOPSIS: VAL'S LONG STRUGGLE IN THE ICY WATER OF THE MARSH LEFT HIM WEAK AND EXHAUSTED AND FOR DAYS NOW HE HAS TOSSED IN A FEVER FIGHTING FOR EVERY BREATH.

AT LAST YOUTH AND STRENGTH TRIUMPH AND HE LIES WEAK AND PALE, BUT BREATHING EASIER—AND SOON—

THE GRIZZLED VETERANS HOLD A FEAST IN HONOR OF VAL'S GREATEST FIGHT—HIS VICTORY OVER GRANDFATHER DEATH.

A WARM, PERSISTENT SOUTH WIND LOOSENS WINTER'S GRIP ON THE GREAT MARSHES, LIFE AWAKENS AND IN VAL'S MIND GREAT PLANS ARE COMPLETED.

HE CALLS AN ASSEMBLY AND TO THE EXILED KING DECLAIMS:—"TOO LONG HAVE OUR GOOD SWORDS RUSTED, OH! MY FATHER, WHILE THE PEOPLE OF THULE GROAN BENEATH THE HEEL OF A CRUEL TYRANT—WE ARE BUT TWENTY AGAINST AN ARMY, BUT WE WILL FIGHT, AS EVANGELISTS, PREACHING THE RETURN OF JUSTICE AND FREEDOM AND GATHER AN ARMY AS WE GO; AS RIGHTFUL KING, YOU WILL LEAD US TO WHATEVER FATE AWAITS."

FIRED BY VAL'S ENTHUSIASM THEY DRAW UP PLANS, WHILE THE HAPPY VETERANS REPAIR THEIR GEAR.

12-4-38

VAL STARTS MAPPING THE CHANNELS BY WHICH A CHARTERED SHIP MIGHT APPROACH THEIR ISLAND FROM THE SEA.

BUT OTHERS ARE EXPLORING THE FENS, TOO!
—NEXT WEEK—
"THE SAXON INVASION OF ENGLAND"

VAL PLANS TO CONQUER THE TYRANT AND PLACE HIS FATHER BACK UPON THE THRONE OF THULE. WHILE SEEKING A CHANNEL UP WHICH A SHIP MAY COME TO TAKE THEM FROM THEIR ISLAND OF EXILE THE YOUNG PRINCE MEETS A PARTY OF SAXONS.

FROM THE CORNER OF HIS EYE VAL SEES THE SPEAR FLASH IN THE SUNLIGHT ——!

"I MUST HAVE GOT HIM, HE DOES NOT RISE," SAYS THE SAXON LEADER, AS THEY WAIT A FULL QUARTER-HOUR.

BUT A LIFE OF DANGER HAS TAUGHT VAL MANY TRICKS —— AFTER THEY DEPART HE RIGHTS HIS DUGOUT——

AND FOLLOWS, SEEKING THE REASON FOR SAXON SCOUTS IN THE ENGLISH FENS.

WHERE MARSH AND SEA MEET VAL IS ASTONISHED TO SEE A GREAT FLEET OF THREE HUNDRED SAXON SHIPS COVERING THE WATERS OF THE WIDE BAY.

RUSHING HOME WITH THE NEWS VAL CRIES—"THE SAXONS INVADE BRITIAN—AMBUSH ALL SCOUTS. I GO TO WARN KING ARTHUR!"

AND DRIVES HIS LIGHT CANOE SWIFTLY TOWARD THE MAINLAND AND HIS FRIEND, THE SHEPHERD BOY.

12-11-38

"QUICK! MY SADDLE AND HORSES! THE SAXONS COME!"

"SUMMON ALL THE FENS' PEOPLE AND BID THEM HARRY THE ENEMY SCOUTS THAT THEY MAY GATHER NO INFORMATION. I RIDE TO CAMELOT!"

NEXT WEEK—HORSE-TRADING

GOADING HIS WIRY LITTLE HORSES TO THEIR UTMOST SPEED VAL GALLOPS THROUGH THE NIGHT. THOUGH HE CHANGES FROM ONE TO THE OTHER OFTEN, ERE DAWN THEY ARE COMPLETELY EXHAUSTED.

AT SUNRISE HE MEETS A WELL-MOUNTED KNIGHT AND HIS LADY.

"I CARRY A MESSAGE OF GREAT IMPORTANCE TO THE KING, LEND ME A HORSE!" "AND BE A VICTIM OF A COMMON HORSE-THIEF?" SNARLS THE KNIGHT.

BUT VAL HAD EXPECTED SUCH AN ANSWER AND HAS ONE OF HIS IMPISH TRICKS READY.

WHILE THE ANGRY KNIGHT TRIES TO DISENGAGE THE TANGLED REINS VAL SWIFTLY BUT GENTLY LIFTS THE INDIGNANT DAME FROM HER PALFREY —

AND GALLOPS AWAY ON HIS MISSION!

AN HOUR LATER VAL HEARS HOOF-BEATS AND TURNS TO SEE THE ENRAGED KNIGHT IN HOT PURSUIT, HIS GREAT WAR-HORSE GAINING RAPIDLY ON THE FAT PALFREY.

"SUCH HASTE IS UNDIGNIFIED, EVEN IN A KING'S MESSENGER," MUTTERS VAL AS HE URGES HIS LABORING MOUNT TO KEEP AHEAD OF THE GLEAMING LANCE-POINT.

NEXT WEEK — THE NOISY ARRIVAL

12-18-38

SYNOPSIS: SO FAST DOES VAL RIDE WITH NEWS OF THE SAXON'S LANDING THAT HIS HORSES DROP. A KNIGHT AND HIS LADY REFUSE TO LEND ONE OF THEIRS, BUT VAL TRICKS THE KNIGHT, LIFTS THE INDIGNANT DAME FROM HER FAT PALFREY AND GALLOPS AWAY — THE KNIGHT IN PURSUIT.

AND RIGHT THROUGH THE GATES OF CAMELOT HE CHASES THE YOUNG HORSE-THIEF.

"NOW I'LL GET HIM," MUTTERS THE ANGRY KNIGHT, "HE DARE NOT RIDE PAST THE PALACE GATES."

BUT VAL CANNOT STOP ON THE POLISHED FLOORS AND A TANGLED MASS OF GUARDS, HORSE AND RIDER SLIDE TOWARD THE THRONE!

"I MIGHT HAVE GUESSED," SAYS THE ASTONISHED KING, "WHO ELSE BUT PRINCE VALIANT WOULD ARRIVE LIKE THAT!"

UNTANGLING HIMSELF FROM THE STRUGGLING HEAP VAL KNEELS BEFORE THE THRONE. "SIRE, I BRING TIDINGS OF A SAXON INVASION . . . . . ."

. . . . ."AND RUIN TO OUR POLISHED FLOORS," ROARS THE KING, HIS EYES TWINKLING. "NINE SAXON INVASIONS HAVE BROUGHT LESS DAMAGE TO CAMELOT THAN ONE ARRIVAL OF PRINCE VALIANT."

. . . . ."NOR WILL THE SAXONS EVER DAMAGE CAMELOT WHILE IT IS DE-FENDED BY GOOD KING ARTHUR!"

"MERLIN, WHAT SHALL WE DO WITH THIS KNAVE WHO BUTTERS US WITH FLATTERY TO TURN ASIDE OUR WRATH? CAN'T WE GIVE HIM TO THE SAXONS THAT HE MAY DRIVE THEM TO MADNESS?"

12-25-38

THEN THE KING ARISES, ALL SERIOUS, AND CALLS HIS COUNCIL OF WAR TO MAKE PLANS FOR THE TENTH DEFENSE OF BRITAIN AGAINST THE SAXON INVADER.

NEXT WEEK—THE INDIGNANT DAME

HAL FOSTER

WHEN PRINCE VALIANT DASHES INTO CAMELOT WITH NEWS OF A SAXON INVASION KING ARTHUR IMMEDIATELY CALLS THE GRAND COUNCIL OF WAR INTO SESSION. VAL'S HASTE HAS EXHAUSTED HIS OWN HORSE AND HE FINDS IT NECESSARY TO STEAL A LADY'S PALFREY TO FINISH HIS JOURNEY AND HAS BEEN PURSUED ALL THE WAY BY HER ENRAGED HUSBAND, WHO, IN HIS ANGER, FORGETS ALL ABOUT HIS ABANDONED WIFE.....

AN HOUR LATER AND INTO CAMELOT COMES THE FUMING LADY, DESERTED IN THE FOREST, RIDING ASTRIDE A MAN'S SADDLE, HER DIGNITY HURT.....

AS HIS ANGER COOLED SIR KNIGHT BETHINKS HIM OF THE WIFE HE HAS ABANDONED IN THE FOREST — BUT TOO LATE.

NOW, WHEN A LONG-SUFFERING WIFE, WHO HAS WORKED HER FINGERS TO THE BONE FOR AN UNAPPRECIATIVE HUSBAND, FEELS IT HER DUTY TO GIVE THE WRETCH A GOOD TALKING TO — FOR HIS OWN GOOD, OF COURSE.....

.....AND THE SIGHT OF HIM IN COMPANY WITH A HORSE-THIEF REMINDS HER OF OTHER THINGS THAT SHOULD BE MENTIONED.....

.....NOT EVEN THE ANNOYANCE OF A KING CAN HALT THE FLOW OF REALLY CONSTRUCTIVE CRITICISM!

SOFTLY KING ARTHUR DRAWS THE CURTAINS—"LET US HASTEN OUR PLANS THAT WE MAY FIND THE COMPARATIVE PEACE OF THE BATTLE-FIELD!" (FOR HE, TOO, IS A MARRIED MAN).

AND SO THE COUNCIL RESUMES ITS PLANS FOR THE TENTH WAR AGAINST THE SAXONS.

1-1-39

"THEY HARBOR IN THE FENS," SAYS MERLIN, "WHO KNOWS AUGHT OF THESE WASTES?" THEN ARISES SIR GAWAIN, "NO ONE IN ALL ENGLAND KNOWS THEM AS DOES PRINCE VALIANT."

AND SO VAL IS SUMMONED TO KING ARTHUR'S COUNCIL OF WAR.
·NEXT WEEK·
BATTLE PLANS

SO VAL IS CALLED AND FOR THE FIRST TIME A HUMBLE SQUIRE BECOMES ONE OF THE GRAND COUNCIL.

"PRINCE VALIANT, YOU HAVE LIVED IN THE FENS, TELL US ALL YOU KNOW OF THE INVADERS' POSITION AND HOW WE CAN MEET THEM."

TAKING A CHARRED STICK FROM THE FIREPLACE, VAL STEPS UPON A TABLE AND DRAWS A MAP OF THE FENS ON THE WALL.

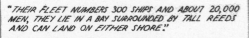

"THEIR FLEET NUMBERS 300 SHIPS AND ABOUT 20,000 MEN, THEY LIE IN A BAY SURROUNDED BY TALL REEDS AND CAN LAND ON EITHER SHORE."

AND LISTENING TO THE YOUNG WARRIOR'S WORDS ARE THE GREAT NOBLES OF THE KING'S COUNCIL OF WAR —
FIRST, WISE MERLIN
LAUNCELOT, THE COURTEOUS
MIGHTY TRISTRAM
ULFIUS AND BRASTIAS, THE EVER FAITHFUL
BEDIVERE, WHO SERVED HIS KING TO THE END

KAY, THE SENESCHAL
GAWAIN, THE LIGHT-HEARTED
SIR MODRED, WHO LATER BECOMES A TRAITOR
SIR ECTOR, KING'S GUARDIAN.

"SIRE, THE SAXONS NUMBER 20,000, WE CAN MUSTER BUT 10,000 IN TIME TO OPPOSE A LANDING — TO DEFEND BOTH SHORES WOULD SPLIT OUR ARMY AND WEAKEN IT, OUR SHIPS ARE TOO FEW — BUT I HAVE A PLAN!"

WITH THE KING'S PERMISSION THE DARING LAD UNFOLDS AN IMPISH SCHEME OF SUCH AUDACITY THAT THE NOBLE LORDS OF THE COUNCIL SHOUT WITH APPROVAL.

THEN FROM THE SEVEN GATES OF CAMELOT SPEED THE KING'S COURIERS TO SUMMON ALL TO WAR!
—NEXT WEEK—
THE SMOKE SCREEN

SYNOPSIS: TO DELAY THE LANDING OF THE INVADING SAXON ARMY VAL AROUSED THE FENS' PEOPLE TO HAMPER THE SCOUTS. THE PLAN HE SUBMITTED TO THE KING HAS BEEN ACCEPTED AND THE KNIGHTS OF ENGLAND GATHER TO DEFEND THE REALM.

UNDER A STARLESS SKY THE BRILLIANT ARMY MOVES TO ITS POSITION SOUTH OF THE BAY.

AT DAWN HORSA, THE SAXON CHIEFTAN, POINTS NORTHWARD TO THE LEVEL PLAIN. "THE BRITONS GATHER THERE, FOR I SEE THE DRAGON HELMET OF ARTHUR AND THE LION SHIELDS OF LAUNCELOT AND TRISTRAM!"

BUT THE FACE OF DAGONET, THE JESTER, LOOKS OUT FROM BENEATH THE KING'S GOLDEN CASQUE AND A SCULLERY LAD AND A STABLE BOY CARRY THE SHIELDS OF LAUNCELOT AND TRISTRAM.

"THEY WISH US TO THINK THE ARMY AWAITS US ON THE SOUTH — BUT WE ARE NOT FOOLED — THOSE ARE BUT DUMMIES."

BUT BEHIND THE DUMMIES THE GLITTERING ARMY AWAITS VAL'S SIGNAL.

THE KING'S SCANTY FLEET, WAITING OUT- SIDE THE BAY, IS GREETED WITH DERISION.

THIS SHORE DEFENDED ONLY BY THE KING'S JESTER AND TWO YOKELS

OCEAN

THE KING'S SMALL FLEET

CAN LAND ON EITHER SHORE

VAL'S GALLANT 500 HIDING IN THESE CHANNELS

VAL'S HOME

20,000 SAXONS

DUMMY DEFENDERS

ARTHUR'S 10,000 KNIGHTS HIDDEN BEHIND THE HILLS

IMPENETRABLE

SWAMPS

(THE FENS)

TO CAMELOT

PLAN OF THE BATTLEFIELD FOR KING ARTHUR'S 10th MEETING WITH THE SAXONS UNDER HORSA.

NEXT WEEK — THE BATTLE

1-15-39

HAL FOSTER

..... AND NOW, — DOWN THE TOR- TUOUS CHANNELS OF THE GREAT SWAMP MOVES A STRANGE FLEET LOADED WITH FIRE-BALLS AND BOUND ON A DARING MISSION.

NEVER HAS SUCH A GREAT SAXON FORCE INVADED BRITAIN — AND NEVER IN A STRONGER POSITION. IN DESPERATION THE KING ADOPTS THE MAD, INGENIOUS PLAN THAT VAL UNFOLDS TO THE GRAND COUNCIL OF WAR. VAL HAS PROMISED THAT, WITH 500 MEN, HE WILL DRIVE 20,000 ARMED SAXON WARRIORS IN PANIC BEFORE ARTHUR'S WAITING ARMY.

VAL SHOUTS A COMMAND, A TRUMPET SOUNDS AND IN A MOMENT THE MARSH IS A MASS OF FLAMES.

THE ASTONISHED SAXONS SEE THE BAY QUICKLY ENCIRCLED ON THREE SIDES BY A LEAPING SHEET OF FLAME — THEN SUDDENLY THEY ARE ENVELOPED IN A DENSE CLOUD OF CHOKING SMOKE.

AND OUT OF THAT SMOKE COMES A SHOWER OF FIRE-BALLS THROWN BY AN INVISIBLE ENEMY!

BURNING RAFTS AND FLAMING CANOES DRIFT WITH THE WIND AMONG THE ANCHORED SHIPS..... FIRE AND CONFUSION ARE EVERYWHERE.

"TO SHORE," SCREAMS HORSA, "THE SOUTH BANK IS DEFENDED ONLY BY DUMMIES, LAND THERE AND REORGANIZE."

1-22-38

VAL HEARS THE COMMAND AND IMMEDIATELY CHANGES HIS ATTACK.

AS THE SAXONS LAND TO REFORM THEIR RANKS A DEADLY SHOWER OF ARROWS COMES OUT OF THE SMOKE AND DRIVES THEM INLAND.

THE INVADERS COME STUMBLING OUT FROM BENEATH THE CLOUD OF STIFLING SMOKE AND STINGING ARROWS AND THERE — DRAWN UP IN BATTLE ARRAY, IS THE KING'S ARMY!

NEXT WEEK PRINCE VALIANT IS KNIGHTED!

HAL FOSTER

SYNOPSIS: WITH BUT 10,000 MEN KING ARTHUR FACES AN ARMY OF 20,000 SAXON WARRIORS. VAL PROMISES TO DELIVER THE INVADERS IN PANIC BEFORE THE KING'S MEN AND, WITH FLAME, SMOKE AND ARROWS, KEEPS HIS PROMISE.

MIGHTY ARE THE DEEDS OF LAUNCELOT, GREAT IS TRISTRAM WITH SWORD AND SHIELD, BUT NONE IS TERRIBLE AS ARTHUR WHEN THEY CHARGE INTO BATTLE SHOUTING!

ON THE BAY AMID THE FLAME AND SMOKE PRINCE VAL AND HIS NIMBLE BAND COMPLETE THE DESTRUCTION OF THE FLEET.

THOSE SHIPS THAT GROPED THEIR WAY OUT THROUGH THE SMOKE FIND THE KING'S FLEET AWAITING THEM.

1-29-39

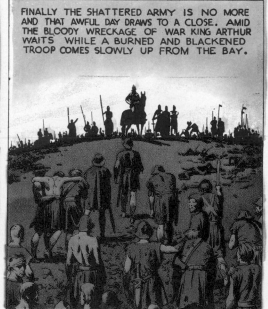

FINALLY THE SHATTERED ARMY IS NO MORE AND THAT AWFUL DAY DRAWS TO A CLOSE. AMID THE BLOODY WRECKAGE OF WAR KING ARTHUR WAITS WHILE A BURNED AND BLACKENED TROOP COMES SLOWLY UP FROM THE BAY.

VAL STANDS BEFORE THE KING. *"ONE DEED IS YET TO BE DONE THIS DAY — KNEEL,"* SAYS ARTHUR DRAWING KEEN EXCALIBUR FROM ITS JEWELLED SCABBARD AND TOUCHING THE GRIMY LAD UPON THE SHOULDER, *"NOW RISE, SIR VALIANT, PRINCE AND KNIGHT OF THE ROUND TABLE!"*

NEXT WEEK:
NEW KINGDOMS

THE SUN SINKS BLOOD-RED BEHIND THE SMOKE OF THE BURNING FLEET AND VICTORIOUS ARTHUR GATHERS HIS HOSTS ABOUT HIM..... AND THERE, AMID THE WRECKAGE OF THAT TERRIBLE FIELD, HE MAKES PRINCE VALIANT A KNIGHT OF THE ROUND TABLE!

TURNING TO VAL'S PROUD FATHER THE KING SAYS "AND YOU, O RIGHTFUL KING OF THULE, ASK WHAT YOU WILL OF ME."

"ONLY ONE OF THE SHIPS WE HAVE CAPTURED THAT WE MAY SAIL ONCE AGAIN TO THULE."

"I HAD FORESEEN YOUR REQUEST, FATHER, AND WAS CAREFUL TO PRESERVE YONDER GOODLY SHIP FROM THE FLAMES."

AS THEY DRESS THEIR BURNS AND WOUNDS AND WASH AWAY THE GRIME OF BATTLE, THE OLD WARRIORS ARE HAPPY IN THE THOUGHT THAT SOON THEY WILL SAIL FOR HOME.

NEXT MORNING THEY GATHER FROM THE BATTLEFIELD ALL THE ARMS AND EQUIPMENT NECESSARY FOR THEIR VENTURE, LOAD THEIR SHIP AND AWAIT THE INCOMING TIDE.

UP THE TWISTING CHANNELS THEY WORK THE SHIP TO THE ISLAND THAT HAS BEEN THEIR HOME DURING 12 YEARS OF EXILE.

THE FINAL PREPARATIONS ARE COMPLETED — THEN HO! FOR THE OPEN SEA!

2-5-39

BEHIND LIES PEACE AND SAFETY IN BRITAIN; AHEAD IS THE UNHAPPY LAND OF THULE IN THE GRIP OF SLIGON, THE TYRANT; DANGER, AND PERHAPS DEATH. BUT TWENTY KEEN SWORDS AND TWENTY STOUT HEARTS ARE PLEDGED TO REGAIN A KINGDOM AND THEIR HOMES.

·NEXT WEEK·
THE CRUSADE

SYNOPSIS: FOR HIS SPLENDID DEEDS IN BATTLE PRINCE VALIANT IS MADE KNIGHT OF THE ROUND TABLE AND GRANTED A SHIP IN WHICH TO SAIL FOR THULE. THEY PLEDGE THEMSELVES TO BANISH THE TYRANT SLIGON AND PLACE VAL'S FATHER BACK ON HIS THRONE.

AT LAST THEY SEE THE FAIR SHORE OF THEIR HOMELAND SPARKLING IN THE SUNLIGHT.

THEY LAND AND STORE THEIR GREAT CARGO OF ARMS IN A FRIENDLY VILLAGE.

THEN THE KING APPLIES A TORCH TO THE SHIP. "WE HAVE BEEN DRIVEN FROM THESE SHORES ONCE, BUT WE HAVE RETURNED NEVERMORE TO LEAVE. WE WILL BRING PEACE TO THE PEOPLE WE LOVE OR FIND PEACE BENEATH THE SOIL WE HONOR."

THEN COME BUSY, DANGEROUS DAYS; SWIFT MESSENGERS RIDING AT NIGHT CARRY TIDINGS OF THE KING'S RETURN.

THE FAITHFUL TWENTY RANGE FAR AND WIDE PROMISING THE ENSLAVED PEASANTS FREEDOM AND JUSTICE UNDER THE KING'S BANNER.

MANY OF THE NOBLES COME TO THE KING SECRETLY AND PLEDGE LOYALTY.

SLOWLY AT FIRST BUT IN EVER INCREASING NUMBERS, RESOLUTE MEN GATHER AT THE KING'S HIDING-PLACE AND ARE ARMED.

VAL, WORKING AMONG THE KNIGHTS AND WARRIORS, HAS MANY A FIGHT.

SLIGON'S SPIES HINDER, BUT CANNOT STOP THE GROWING REVOLT.

MADE BOLD BY HOPE OF DELIVERANCE THE VILLAGERS ATTACK SLIGON'S BRUTAL TAX-GATHERERS.

2-12-39

INTO THIS TROUBLED LAND THE BANNER OF THE RED STALLION COMES LIKE A RAY OF HOPE AND, AS THE DAYS SPEED SWIFTLY BY, THE KING'S CAUSE PROSPERS.

IN HIS CLOSE-GUARDED STRONGHOLD SLIGON BROODS, SICK IN MIND AND BODY, WHILE HIS EVIL POWER MELTS AWAY BEFORE THE EXILED KING'S PLEDGE, "FREEDOM AND JUSTICE!"
NEXT WEEK: "THE BARGAIN"

HAL FOSTER

FOR TWELVE LONG YEARS THE PEOPLE OF THULE HAVE SUFFERED UNDER THE TYRANNY OF SLIGON, SO WHEN THEIR EXILED KING RETURNS IN SECRET AND RAISES ONCE MORE THE BANNER OF THE RED STALLION THEY FLOCK TO HIS SUPPORT UNTIL HIS STRENGTH SOON EQUALS THAT OF SLIGON.

SLIGON'S SOLDIERS ARE CALLED IN TO PROTECT HIS STRONGHOLD.

AND NOW THE HOUR HAS COME! THE KING PREPARES TO MARCH.

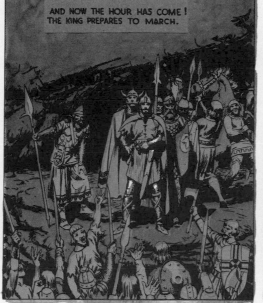

BUT A MESSENGER GALLOPS UP CRYING, "SLIGON WILL DISCUSS TERMS WITH PRINCE VALIANT AND GUARANTEE HIS SAFETY IF HE DARE COME."

THE COUNCIL, WELL-USED TO SLIGON'S TREACHERY, ADVISE AGAINST IT, BUT VAL DECIDES TO GO ON THE OFF CHANCE THAT SOMEHOW THE MEN OF THULE MAY BE SAVED A RUINOUS WAR.

ALONE HE ENTERS THE ENEMY FORTRESS; A CASTLE HE ONCE CALLED HOME.

2-19-39

"THE KINGDOM OF THULE I TOOK BY FORCE; BY FORCE I HAVE HELD IT, BUT I WEARY OF FORCE, OF CRUELTY, TREACHERY AND DISTRUST. ABOUT ME ARE FAWNING COURTIERS WITH FLATTERING WORDS ON THEIR TONGUES AND HATRED IN THEIR EYES AND I FEAR THESE SILKEN JACKALS — GO TO YOUR FATHER AND SAY: 'SLIGON IS BUT A TIRED HUCKSTER AT HEART AND WILL BARTER THE KINGDOM OF THULE FOR HIS PEACEFUL ISLAND IN THE ENGLISH SWAMPS'."

NEXT WEEK: "VICTORY"

SYNOPSIS: SLIGON WAS ONCE A MIGHTY TYRANT, BUT NOW, WEARY AND SICK, HE OFFERS HIS TOTTERING THRONE TO THE KING IN EXCHANGE FOR A TINY, PEACEFUL ISLAND IN THE QUIET ENGLISH SWAMPS.

WITH THIS WELCOME NEWS VAL GALLOPS TO HIS FATHER'S CAMP AND THE BARGAIN IS MADE AMID GREAT REJOICING.

AS THE RIGHTFUL KING ONCE MORE ENTERS THE GREAT FORTRESS WHERE HE AND HIS FATHERS BEFORE HIM HAD RULED WITH FIRM JUSTICE, SLIGON SLIPS UNNOTICED FROM ANOTHER GATE TO FIND THE PEACE AND QUIET HE HAS NEVER KNOWN.

IN THE PALACE THE KING PLUNGES INTO THE WORK OF REORGANIZING THE HARSH GOVERNMENT AND SMOOTHING OUT OLD INJUSTICES.

TO PRINCE VALIANT FALLS THE TASK OF BRINGING INTO LINE ALL THOSE NOBLES WHO HAVE NOT YET PLEDGED FEALTY TO THE KING.

IN THESE ROUGH DAYS THERE IS BUT ONE WAY TO SETTLE A DISPUTE— THE TRIAL BY ARMS.

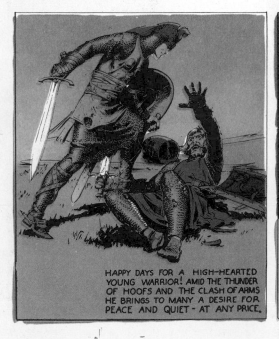

HAPPY DAYS FOR A HIGH-HEARTED YOUNG WARRIOR! AMID THE THUNDER OF HOOFS AND THE CLASH OF ARMS HE BRINGS TO MANY A DESIRE FOR PEACE AND QUIET - AT ANY PRICE.

BUT WHEN SLIGON SAID HE WANTED PEACE HE WAS SINCERE— SO SINCERE IN FACT THAT HE LEAVES HIS WIFE AND DAUGHTER BEHIND.

Copr. 1938, King Features Syndicate, Inc. World rights reserved.   2-26-39

HAL FOSTER

THE BUSY KING PROVIDES THEM WITH APARTMENTS IN A DISTANT WING OF THE CASTLE AND THEN FORGETS THEM, BUT CLARIS IS NOT THE KIND OF GIRL ONE CAN FORGET FOR LONG.

NEXT WEEK "CLARIS"

SYNOPSIS: THE VICTORIOUS KING PROVIDES SLIGON'S ABANDONED WIFE AND DAUGHTER WITH APARTMENTS IN A DISTANT WING OF THE CASTLE AND THEN PROCEEDS TO FORGET ABOUT THEM — BUT PRETTY CLARIS IS NOT ONE TO BE FORGOTTEN FOR LONG.

FOR CLARIS IS AN ARTFUL LITTLE IMP WHO HAS TROUBLED MANY HEARTS — BY WAY OF PRACTICE.

SO WHEN, FROM HER TOWER, SHE SEES PRINCE VALIANT RETURNING SHE TIDIES HER HAIR, PUTS ON HER MOST BECOMING GOWN AND SMILES A THOUGHTFUL SMILE.

FOR VAL IS RETURNING FROM A SIX-MONTHS TOUR OF THE KINGDOM, DURING WHICH HE HAS WON MANY OF SLIGON'S OLD SUPPORTERS OVER TO HIS FATHER'S CAUSE.

NOT WITH FAIR WORDS AND PROMISES, FOR VAL FOUND HE COULD BETTER POINT OUT THEIR ERRORS WITH A LANCE AND DRIVE HOME AN ARGUMENT WITH A SWORD.

IT HAPPENS, JUST BY THE ODDEST CHANCE IMAGINABLE, THAT THESE TWO MEET IN THE GARDEN.

IT IS PLEASANT, AFTER ALL THESE MONTHS OF FIGHTING AND HARD-SHIP, TO BE AT EASE IN A SUN-NY GARDEN WITH SO GAY A COMPANION.

SO THESE TWO YOUNG PEOPLE ARE OFTEN TOGETHER — HE LIKES HER MERRY WIT AND READY LAUGHTER — AND SHE IS CAREFUL TO LOOK HER BEST.

VAL MAKES LIGHT-HEARTED LOVE TO HER, (FOR WHO WOULD BE SO UNGAL-LANT AS TO NEGLECT THE DUTY WE ALL OWE TO BEAUTIFUL LADIES?) BUT HE REFUSES TO TAKE HER SERIOUSLY, FOR THE MEMORY OF HIS TRAGIC ROMANCE WITH ILENE IS STILL FRESH IN HIS HEART. SHE USES ALL HER PRETTY ARTS TO NO AVAIL — IT IS MOST DISCOURAGING.

ONE DAY CLARIS SEES VAL WITH HIS CLOSEST FRIEND, GOOD-NATURED ALFRED DE GERIN, AND SHE HAS AN IDEA — WHY NOT STIR VAL OUT OF HIS GAY INDIFFERENCE WITH JEALOUSY? 3-5-39

AND SO SHE STARTS A LITTLE FLIRTATION WITH SIMPLE ALFRED.

HAL FOSTER

INSTEAD OF KINDLING A SPARK IN PRINCE VALIANT SHE STARTS A RAGING FIRE IN THE HEART OF POOR INNOCENT ALFRED.

NEXT WEEK: A CHALLENGE

CROWN PRINCE VALIANT OF THULE, HOT-TEMPERED, LIGHT-HEARTED, BUT STILL BROODING OVER A TRAGIC ROMANCE, PROVES A DIFFICULT PROBLEM FOR·····

CLARIS WHO WISH-ES TO WED HIM AND BECOME THE FUTURE QUEEN OF THULE. SO FAR ALL HER ARTFUL WILES HAVE PROVED UNAVAILING·····SHE HAS EVEN TRIED TO AWAK-EN HIS JEALOUSY BY A MILD FLIRTATION WITH HIS FRIEND·····

TALL ALFRED WHO PROMPTLY FALLS IN LOVE WITH THE SCHEMING LITTLE MINX, LOSING HIS HEART, HIS APPETITE AND HIS PEACE OF MIND.

SEEING VAL APPROACH, CLARIS PLAYS HER LITTLE GAME FOR HIS BENEFIT.

WITH ASTONISHING RESULTS—CLARIS FINDS HERSELF BEING THOROUGHLY, ARDENTLY AND DELIGHTFULLY KISSED.

VAL IS FURIOUS, "ALFRED, YOUR UNBECOMING CONDUCT DISPLEASES ME!" AND ALFRED, HIS HEAD WHIRL-ING, REPLIES, "YOU WILL FIND ME READY WHEN-EVER YOUR DISPLEASURE TAKES ACTIVE FORM."

CLARIS SITS DOWN·····SHE HAS BEEN KISSED BE-FORE, BUT NEVER QUITE SO EARNESTLY·····AND THAT TALL, BLUNDERING FOOL HAS UPSET HER PLANS, TOO·····HE IS A STUPID OX, EVEN IF HE DOES HAVE NICE EYES. SHE HATES HIM SO MUCH SHE RATHER SUSPECTS SHE IS FALL-ING IN LOVE WITH HIM.

THE TWO LADS ARM THEMSELVES AND REPAIR TO A WOOD—THERE TO SETTLE THE LITTLE MATTER OF THE STOLEN KISS.

POOR ALFRED—EVEN IF HE WINS THE DUEL THE KING WILL PROMPT-LY HANG HIM—CLARIS APPEALS TO THE KING.

THE TWO YOUNG WARRIORS ARE HACKING AT EACH OTHER WITH LUSTY ENTHUSIASM WHEN THE AN-GRY KING PUTS A STOP TO IT. 109 3-12-39

HE BELIEVES CLARIS TO BE A SCHEM-ING LITTLE TROUBLEMAKER AND TELLS VAL SO. VAL'S HOT TEMPER FLARES AND HE TELLS HIS FATHER HE WILL NOT BE BULLIED, EVEN BY A KING AND CAN VERY WELL LOOK AFTER HIS OWN AFFAIRS.

NEXT WEEK: TANGLED AFFAIRS

CLARIS, DAUGHTER OF SLIGON, IS AN AMBITIOUS LITTLE LADY WHO IS DETERMINED TO MARRY CROWN PRINCE VALIANT AND BECOME THE FUTURE QUEEN OF THULE, COST WHAT IT MAY. THE KING FORBIDS VAL TO HAVE ANYTHING TO DO WITH HER AND FATHER AND SON QUARREL.

"SINCE ILENE IS GONE AND I CAN NEVER LOVE AGAIN WHY NOT WED CLARIS? SHE IS PRETTY AND GAY AND WILL KEEP ME FROM BEING LONELY."

SO HE STRAIGHTWAY GOES TO CLARIS AND DEMANDS, "WILL YOU MARRY ME?" "YES",—AND THEN SHE LIES PRETTILY, "FOR I HAVE LOVED YOU FROM THE FIRST."
"FINE...I'LL HAVE HORSES READY AT DAWN FOR WE MUST FLEE THE ANGER OF THE KING."

"WE WILL SPEED TO BRITTANY. THERE WILL BE SOME SPLENDID FIGHTING UNDER KING BAN; THEN TO ENGLAND WITH KING ARTHUR, THERE SHOULD BE SOME SPLENDID BATTLES GOING ON EVEN NOW. OH, WE WILL BE HAPPY."

ONE BY ONE HER DREAM CASTLES TUMBLE ABOUT HER EARS, SHE WANTS TO MARRY A PRINCE, NOT A LIGHT-HEARTED BUTCHER. SHE WANTS TO SIT ON THE THRONE OF THULE, NOT ON A WARHORSE IN FOGGY ENGLAND. IN FACT, WHAT SHE WANTS MOST OF ALL, SHE DECIDES, IS TO BE LOVED BY····

···ALFRED, THAT BLUNDERING, TALL IDIOT, WHO HAS SPOILED ALL HER PLANS BY FALLING IN LOVE WITH HER AND KISSING HER SO ROUGHLY. SHE WONDERS IF HE WILL EVER LEARN ANY BETTER.

SHE GOES TO FIND OUT AND VAL LOOKING INTO THE SUNLIT GARDENS SEES THEM·····LISTENING HE HEARS A SMALL VOICE WAILING·····

"I PROMISED AND I HAVE TO GO, I MAY BE QUEEN SOME DAY IF I DON'T CATCH MY DEATH OF COLD FOLLOWING VAL ALL OVER THOSE DRAUGHTY BATTLEFIELDS AND IT IS UNFAIR OF YOU TO BE SO HANDSOME."

"WELL, STRIKE ME WITH A BATTLE-AX! FATHER WAS RIGHT, THE L..LE TRICKSTER! FANCY HER WANTING TO BE QUEEN OF THULE WHEN SHE CAN RULE THE HEART OF A LAD LIKE ALFRED... I'LL FIX HER."

Copr. 1939, King Features Syndicate, Inc., World rights reserved   3-19-59

POOR LOVELORN ALFRED IS ON THE BRINK OF DESPAIR WHEN VAL FINDS HIM AND UNFOLDS A LITTLE SCHEME.
NEXT WEEK: TRICKING A TRICKSTER

SYNOPSIS: POOR LITTLE CLARIS, SHE WORKED AND SCHEMED SO CLEVERLY TO BECOME THE BRIDE OF PRINCE VALIANT AND THE FUTURE QUEEN OF THULE, ONLY TO FALL IN LOVE WITH THE LAD WHOSE HEART SHE HAS BROKEN, EARN THE DIS- PLEASURE OF THE KING AND BECOME PLEDGED TO ELOPE WITH VAL AND LEAVE THULE.

AT LAST THE DAWN, AND THE UNHAPPY GIRL PREPARES TO FACE THE TANGLE SHE HAS CREATED.

VAL GREETS HIS SHIVERING FIANCEE WITH BOISTEROUS GOOD-NATURE.

HE LAUGHS AND SINGS AS IF THE RAIN, THE MUD AND THE COLD ARE MUCH TO HIS LIKING, AS SHE BECOMES MORE MISERABLE HE GROWS MORE AND MORE CHEERFUL.

"WHAT A WONDERFUL ROMANCE OURS WILL BE; SIDE BY SIDE THROUGH SUN AND COLD WE WILL RIDE FROM ONE SPLENDID BATTLEFIELD TO ANOTHER- YOU SHALL COOK FOR ME, TEND MY WOUNDS AND EVERY DAY I WILL BRING YOU THE HEAD OF SOME CONQUERED FOE!" SHE SHUDDERS.

"IT GROWS DARK AND WE HAVE HAD NO MEAL THIS DAY - LET'S TAKE SHELTER IN YONDER CASTLE EVEN THOUGH I HAVE TO KILL ITS OWNER!" AND HE BURSTS OUT LAUGHING.

"WHAT A FOOL I AM," THINKS CLARIS, "TO GIVE UP THE LOVE OF TALL, CLUMSY ALFRED TO BE NURSEMAID TO THIS BLOODTHIRSTY GYPSY — OH! HOW I WISH THAT GATE WOULD FALL ON HIS HEAD!"

"CLARIS, MEET THE NEW OWNER OF THE CASTLE!" CRIES VAL ENTERING, AND WHO SHOULD HURRY FORWARD BUT ALFRED! 111 - 3-26-39

"WE HAVE HAD A WONDERFUL JOURNEY, ALFRED MY FRIEND, BUT SOMETHING TELLS ME CLARIS HAS CEASED TO THINK OF KINGS AND QUEENS AND WANTS ONLY . . . ."
BUT ALFRED IS NO LONGER LISTENING, ONLY LOOKING DIVINELY HAPPY AND VERY, VERY FOOLISH AS MOST LOVERS DO.

NEXT WEEK: PEACE

Knight Errant

SYNOPSIS: THE FRIAR UTTERS A FEW WORDS AND CLARIS IS NO LONGER A MENACE TO THE THRONE AND ALFRED BECOMES A MARRIED MAN ··· CUPID HAS MADE A SIMPERING IDIOT OF THE BOISTEROUS, TALL ROGUE WHOSE RINGING LAUGH AND CLASHING SWORD HAD KEPT THULE BUSY.

VAL IS DISGUSTED ~ A GOOD FIGHTING MAN HAS BEEN SPOILED TO MAKE JUST ANOTHER HUSBAND.

VAL RIDES HOMEWARD THROUGH A SUNNY PEACEFUL LAND.

YES, A PEACEFUL LAND NOW ··· WHERE HEARTY YOUNG WARRIORS WEAR THEIR ARMOR ON A PEG.

FOR THE KING IS ALMOST TOO LENIENT FOR HIS TIMES AND ONLY ORDERS SUCH MURDERS AND EXECUTIONS AS ARE FOR THE PUBLIC GOOD, NEVER FOR PRIVATE PLEASURE ~ AND HIS PEOPLE GRUMBLE AT THE LACK OF ENTERTAINMENT.

EACH MORNING VAL TRAINS WITH THE OTHER KNIGHTS IN THE PALACE COURTYARD.

THE AFTERNOONS ARE SPENT MUCH AS HANDSOME PRINCES SPEND THEM EVERYWHERE.

VAL'S EVENINGS ARE MOST INTERESTING. SCHOLARS, POETS, TRAVELERS AND PHILOSOPHERS GATHER IN HIS ROOMS FOR DISCUSSION AND HE LEARNS MANY CURIOUS THINGS.

4-2-39

EVERY SATURDAY A GAY TOURNAMENT IS HELD AFTER WHICH THE SURVIVORS FEAST MERRILY.

IN FACT, IT IS AN IDEAL KINGDOM WHERE JUSTICE, PROSPERITY AND PEACE REIGN ~ AND VAL IS BORED.

SYNOPSIS: PEACE NOW REIGNS IN THULE AND THE MERCHANTS AND FARMERS ENJOY A PROSPERITY NOT OFTEN FOUND IN THESE ROUGH TIMES. THE WARRIORS ARE KEPT BUSY WITH FREQUENT TOURNAMENTS.

VAL PROFITS BY EVERY OPPORTUNITY TO IMPROVE HIS SKILL.

BUT HE LONGS FOR THOSE JOYOUS, TURBULENT DAYS UNDER KING ARTHUR.

SO HE GOES TO HIS FATHER AND TELLS HIM HE IS GOING TO SEEK ADVENTURE IN FAR COUNTRIES.

"YOU WILL DO NOTHING OF THE SORT," STORMS THE KING. "IT IS YOUR DUTY TO STAY HERE, LEARN STATECRAFT AND GOVERNMENT AND PREPARE YOURSELF FOR THE THRONE!"

"YES, FATHER—BUT YOU PREPARED YOURSELF IN QUITE ANOTHER WAY, FOR THEY STILL TELL OF YOUR BOISTEROUS YOUTH WHEN YOU BROKE LADIES' HEARTS AND MEN'S HEADS ALL ACROSS THE LAND."

"BUT MY FATHER WISHES ME TO STAY AT COURT AND BECOME A SMOOTH COURTIER AND A LOVELY DANCER—NOW, JUST WHERE DID I LEAVE MY SEWING-BASKET?"

SO VAL STRAIGHTWAY GOES AND DOES JUST AS HE HAS PLANNED ALL ALONG....

4-9-39

....AND RIDES FROM THE CASTLE IN SEARCH OF ADVENTURE.

HAL FOSTER

THE KING WATCHES HIS IMPUDENT, HEADSTRONG SON RIDE AWAY—JUST AS HE, HIMSELF, HAD DONE SO MANY YEARS AGO.

NEXT WEEK
KNIGHT ERRANTRY

SYNOPSIS – SO PRINCE VALIANT DEFIES HIS FATHER, BECOMES KNIGHT ERRANT AND GOES GAILY ADVENTURING, AND AFTER HIS LEAVING, THE NOISY COURT BECOMES QUIET, VERY QUIET.

"IT SEEMS", SAYS THE OBSERVANT KING, *"THAT I AM NOT THE ONLY ONE WHO MISSES THE IMPUDENT RASCAL."*

MEANWHILE, VAL IS WANDERING HAPPILY AFIELD, READY FOR ANY ADVENTURE THAT MIGHT TURN UP.

A WANDERER'S HARDSHIPS ARE MANY, BUT HE ENJOYS THE FREEDOM.

ONE DAY VAL CHANCES UPON THE WORK OF BRUTAL ROBBERS — FILLED WITH RAGE HE GIVES CHASE.....

..... AND OVERTAKES THEM IN A FOREST GLADE

LATER, WHILE WIPING OFF HIS SWORD. HE NOTICES FOR THE FIRST TIME THAT A STORM APPROACHES.

THE CAVE OF TIME

.....AND SO SEEKS SHELTER IN A NEARBY CAVE.

– 4 -86-39

HE IS PREPARING TO SPEND THE NIGHT WITHIN THIS SHELTER WHEN HE IS STARTLED BY AN OMINOUS COUGH. TURNING HE FINDS HE IS NOT ALONE .....

NEXT WEEK The WITCH WOMAN

SYNOPSIS—VAL TAKES REFUGE FROM A STORM IN WHAT HE BELIEVES IS AN EMPTY CAVE. HEARING A SLIGHT COUGH HE TURNS, STARTLED, TO FIND A STRANGE WOMAN STANDING BEHIND HIM.

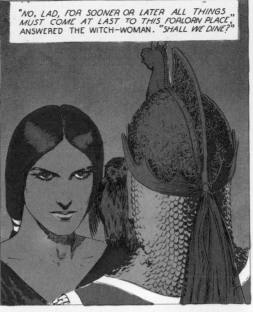

"NO, LAD, FOR SOONER OR LATER ALL THINGS MUST COME AT LAST TO THIS FORLORN PLACE," ANSWERED THE WITCH-WOMAN. "SHALL WE DINE?"

"I DO NOT UNDERSTAND THE MEANING OF YOUR WORDS, BUT YOUR WINE IS POTENT, ALREADY MY HEAD SWIMS."

"THIS CAVE IS THE TROPHY-ROOM OF 'TIME' WHICH NO ONE DARE ENTER."

"I'LL DARE ANY ADVENTURE!" AND DRAWING THE 'SINGING SWORD', VAL ENTERS THE SILENT GLOOM.

A BLUE AND SINISTER GLOW ILLUMINATES THIS MISCHANCY PLACE. IN A FAR CORNER THE BENT FIGURE OF AN AGED MAN CAN BE DIMLY SEEN.

"WHO ARE YOU?" FALTERS THE SCARED YOUTH. "I AM THE ULTIMATE CONQUEROR OF ALL THINGS AND MY TROPHIES ARE THE ALTARS OF FORGOTTEN GODS, THE THRONES OF KINGS, SPLENDID CITIES AND FORTRESSES UNCONQUERABLE."

"NONE MAY WITHSTAND 'TIME'.... I VANQUISH THEM ALL IN THE END.... WOULD YOU CARE TO WRESTLE WITH ME?"

NEXT WEEK: THE CONTEST

SYNOPSIS: IN THE SHELTER OF A GREAT CAVE VAL MEETS A WITCH-WOMAN WHO GIVES HIM A POTENT DRINK AND A GRIM WARNING, WHICH HE IGNORES AND ENTERS THE ABODE OF "TIME."

"YOU DON'T BELIEVE THAT 'TIME' IS UNCONQUERABLE...THEN SHALL WE WRESTLE?"

THE STALWART YOUTH PICKS UP THE SENILE OLD MAN TO FLING HIM AMONG HIS DUSTY TROPHIES.

BUT THE ANCIENT CREATURE CLINGS TENACIOUSLY WITH WEAK, FRAIL HANDS, AS VAL STRIVES TO FREE HIMSELF.

HOW LONG THEY STRUGGLED IN THAT WEIRD, DIM PLACE VAL COULD NEVER AFTERWARDS TELL, BUT HE GROWS WEARY... WEARY....

WITH A CACKLING LAUGH "TIME" HURLS HIS SKINNY ADVERSARY AMONG THE WORLD'S DISCARDED TOYS.

AS VAL STUMBLES OUT OF THAT FANTASTIC CAVERN HE HEARS A THIN, CRACKED VOICE GLOATING, "ALL CONTEND WITH 'TIME' AND ALL ARE VANQUISHED."

AT THE CAVE'S MOUTH THE WITCH-WOMAN CALMLY WAITS THE RETURN OF ALL THAT REMAINS OF A PROUD PRINCE.

"YOU MUST BE TIRED, GRANDFATHER. SIT DOWN AND REFRESH YOURSELF."

VAL DRAINS THE CUP.

NEXT WEEK: THE WANDERER

SYNOPSIS: THE WITCH-WOMAN GIVES VAL A POTENT DRINK AND A WARNING WHICH HE IGNORES. ENTERING THE CAVE HE WRESTLES WITH TIME AND IS VANQUISHED.

"DRINK AND BE REFRESHED POOR, RECKLESS FOOL." THE WEARY OLD PRINCE GRASPS THE GOBLET.

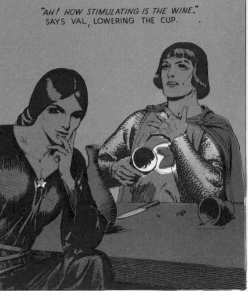

"AH! HOW STIMULATING IS THE WINE." SAYS VAL, LOWERING THE CUP.

THEN TERROR SEIZES HIM AND HE FLEES "TIS A HORRIBLE TRICK, NO SUCH THING COULD POSSIBLY HAVE HAPPENED!"

"HOW TERRIBLE TO BE OLD AND WEAK AND HOW GOOD IT IS TO BE YOUNG AND STRONG AGAIN — I MUST REMEMBER THAT."

HE RIDES FAR AND COMES TO THE SEA OVER WHICH A GREAT STORM IS APPROACHING.

LIGHTS SHINING THROUGH THE STORM PROMISE SHELTER.

HE FINDS A TAVERN FREQUENTED BY SAILORS AND TRAVELERS FROM FAR, STRANGE LANDS.

5-7-39

AS THE STORM WITHOUT RAGES, WEIRD TALES ARE TOLD OF FABULOUS ISLES AND WONDROUS WALLED CITIES.

AND ALL THIS WHILE A HAGGARD WANDERER IS NEARING THE TAVERN WITH ASTOUNDING NEWS.

NEXT WEEK "ROME HAS FALLEN!"

HAL FOSTER

SYNOPSIS: WHILE RIDING AT ADVENTURE AS KNIGHT ERRANT, VAL HAS STRANGE EXPERIENCES. TO-NIGHT HE SHELTERS FROM THE STORM IN A TAVERN AND HEARS WONDROUS TALES OF FAR, STRANGE LANDS.

THERE COMES A POUNDING AT THE DOOR AND IN FROM THE STORM COMES A BATTERED WANDERER.

"ROME HAS FALLEN TO ATTILA AND TO THE SOUTH ALL EUROPE IS IN FLAMES, AS THE HUNS RAVAGE AND KILL."

"BUT ANDELKRAG STILL STANDS, UP ABOVE THE SMOKE AND FLAMES SOAR THE TOWERS OF ANDELKRAG, THE UNCONQUERABLE."

VAL DRAWS THE HAGGARD WANDERER TO A SEAT BESIDE HIM — "*TELL ME OF THIS UNCONQUERABLE FORTRESS*"

"TO THE FORTRESS OF ANDELKRAG, PRINCE CAMERON OF-THE-HIGH-HEAD GATHERS ALL WHO LOVE BEAUTY, MUSIC, POETRY AND NOBLE DEEDS. OFTEN HAS HE BEEN ASSAILED, BUT WHEN HIS LAUGHING WARRIORS MAN THE BATTLEMENT VICTORY IS THEIRS····TROUBADORS EVERYWHERE SING OF CAMERON'S DEEDS···· NOW ONLY ANDELKRAG STANDS ABOVE THE SMOKE OF BURNING EUROPE."

THEN, LAUGHING HORRIBLY, THE WANDERER CHOKES AND FALLS DEAD.

- 5-14-39

"*THE RED PLAGUE*"! WHISPERS A SEAMAN AND ALL RUSH OUT INTO THE NIGHT

THE INN-KEEPER SETS FIRE TO THE TAVERN AND ALL HIS POSSESSIONS. THEN HE, TOO, TAKES FLIGHT AND DISAPPEARS IN THE HOWLING DARKNESS.

NEXT WEEK —"FLIGHT"

Synopsis: FROM A DYING WANDERER VAL HEARS A RUMOR OF THE FALL OF ROME AND THE RAVAGE OF ALL EUROPE BY ATTILA AND HIS HUNS---ONLY BRAVE CAMORAN IN HIS CASTLE ANDELKRAG HOLDS OUT AGAINST THE SAVAGE

"WHAT COULD BE MORE SPLENDID THAN TO FIGHT SIDE BY SIDE WITH GALLANT CAMORAN!" AND VAL TURNS TO THE SOUTHEAST.

LEAVING HIS FATHERS KINGDOM HE RIDES MANY DAYS UNTIL FLEEING REFUGEES AND THE SMOKE OF BURNING VILLAGES GIVE WARNING OF THE HUNS' PRESENCE

NEVER HAS EUROPE BEEN MORE TERRIBLY VISITED VAL SUFFERS SEVERELY FROM THE LACK OF FOOD.

ONCE A BAND OF WANDERING HUNS SWEEPS DOWN ON THE YOUNG KNIGHT AND THERE IS NO ESCAPE.

HIS HEAVIER ARMOR SAVES HIM FROM SERIOUS HURT AND HIS FOES MELT AWAY BEFORE THE FLAMING CIRCLE OF THE "SINGING SWORD."

CUTTING A PLENTIFUL SUPPLY OF HORSE MEAT VAL LEAVES THE DANGEROUS PLAINS AND FINDS A WAY THROUGH THE MOUNTAINS.

FROM A REFUGEE HE LEARNS THAT EMPEROR VALENTINIAN HAS PURCHASED A SHAMEFUL PEACE FOR ROME BY GIVING HIS SISTER AS WIFE TO BRUTAL ATTILA.

- 5 - 21 - 39

PRINCE VAL SHARES HIS FOOD AND THE GRATEFUL MAN GUIDES HIM ACROSS A HAZARDOUS PASS.

AND THERE, BELOW THEM, IS ANDELKRAG, ITS TOWERS RISING ABOVE THE SMOKE AND TURMOIL OF BATTLE.

NEXT WEEK
"THROUGH THE LINES"

PRINCE VALIANT HAS RIDDEN FAR AND DANGEROUSLY
TO COME AT LAST TO ANDELKRAG. AND NOW BELOW HIM
STANDS CAMORAN'S FAR-FAMED FORTRESS SURROUNDED BY
THE INVADING HUNS. HOW CAN HE ALONE ENTER A CASTLE
THAT HAS FOR MONTHS DEFIED THE MIGHT OF ATTILA?

LONG HE STUDIES BEFORE
A PLAN IS FORMED. THEN
GIVING HIS BELOVED WAR-
HORSE INTO THE KEEPING
OF HIS GUIDE, HE STRIDES
DOWN THE SLOPE.

HE HAS ALMOST REACHED
THE MOAT WHEN HIS WAY
IS BARRED BY A RAFT PILED
HIGH WITH FUEL.

- 5 - 28 - 39

IT IS A FIRE-RAFT WITH WHICH, ON THE
MORROW, THE HUNS HOPE TO BURN AWAY
THE DRAW-BRIDGE AND GATE OF ANDELKRAG.
WITH FLINT AND STEEL ......

CIRCLING THE ENEMY CAMP
IN THE DARKNESS, VAL ENTERS
THE RIVER THAT FILLS THE
CASTLE MOAT.

... VAL DESTROYS THEIR WORK.
"TREACHERY", THEY CRY AND
SEARCH FIERCELY FOR THE
CULPRIT!

NEXT WEEK:
CAMORAN

Synopsis: FINDING A FIRE RAFT WITH WHICH THE HUNS HOPE TO BURN AWAY THE OAKEN GATES OF ANDELKRAG, VAL SETS IT ALIGHT.

THE ANGRY HUNS COME RUN-NING TO FIND THE CULPRIT.

CROUCHED NEAR THE BANK VAL COVERS HIM-SELF WITH MUD AS THE SEARCH COMES CLOSER.

SUDDENLY THE DRAW-BRIDGE COMES DOWN WITH A CLANG AND CAMORAN AND HIS WARRIORS DASH FORTH, SHOUTING.

INTO THE CONFUSED HUNS THEY SWEEP LIKE A SCYTHE AMONG WHEAT.

SWIFTLY VAL WADES TO THE BRIDGE AND HAILS THE GUARD. *"I AM PRINCE VALIANT, KNIGHT OF THE ROUND TABLE COME TO JOIN YOUR RANKS."*

THAT HE IS INDEED EVERY INCH A PRINCE NO MAN CAN DOUBT!

THEN CAMORAN RETURNS WITH HIS MEN, LAUGHING AT THE CONFUSION OF THE ENEMY.

- 6 - 4 - 39

"HELLO, YOUNGSTER," HE GRINS. *"FIGHT HARD, SING MERRILY AND YOU WILL BE WELCOME."*

"TO OUR NEW COMPANION — MAY HE CARVE A NAME FOR HIMSELF WITH THAT GREAT SHINING SWORD."

NEXT WEEK: **THE DAY'S WORK**

Synopsis: VAL SLIPS THROUGH THE HORDES OF BESIEGING HUNS AND JOINS THE GALLANT DEFENDERS OF ANDELKRAG UNDER THEIR PRINCE, BRAVE CAMORAN.

AT DAWN THE NIGHT-WATCH DESCENDS AND THE WARRIORS MAN THE BATTLEMENTS.

...AND THEY GO INTO THE FRAY, SINGING THEIR BATTLE CHANTS AND LAUGHING AS THEY FIGHT

NOTHING SEEMS TO DAMPEN THE HIGH SPIRITS OF THESE COURAGEOUS PEOPLE.

THE HUNS ARE LIKE DEMONS IN THEIR FURIOUS ATTACK AND THE WEEKS GO BY LIKE A LONG NIGHTMARE.

HAL FOSTER

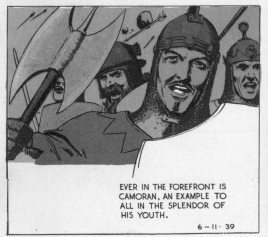

EVER IN THE FOREFRONT IS CAMORAN, AN EXAMPLE TO ALL IN THE SPLENDOR OF HIS YOUTH.

6-11-39

...AND WHEN NIGHT SILENCES THE ATTACK, THE DAY'S SURVIVORS DINE NOBLY WITH SONG AND GAY MUSIC.

NEXT WEEK—
"THE BATTLE"

Synopsis: ATTILA AND HIS ROMAN BRIDE RETIRE INTO PANNONIA, WHICH IS NOW KNOWN AS HUNGARY, BUT HIS FOLLOWERS SWARM IN UNCOUNTED NUMBERS ABOUT UNCONQUERABLE ANDELKRAG.

THE TIRELESS HUNS DIVERT THE RIVER AND DRY UP THE CASTLE MOAT.

WITH THE MOAT FILLED IN, HUGE SIEGE TOWERS LURCH PONDEROUSLY FORWARD.

BUT THE DEFENDERS ROCK THEM BACK AND FORTH WITH GRAPPLES UNTIL THEY FALL CRASHING TO EARTH.

THEN HUGE PROTECTED BATTERING RAMS ARE MOVED AGAINST THE WALLS.

DAY AND NIGHT IS HEARD THE STEADY THUD OF THE RAMS UNTIL AT LAST THE WALL CRUMBLES.

THE HUNS RUSH THROUGH ONLY TO FIND AN INNER WALL BUILT AROUND THE WEAK PLACE.

WELL-PLANNED SORTIES THRUST OUT LIKE A SWORD INTO THE HUN'S CAMP, BURNING AND DESTROYING AND RETURNING AS SWIFTLY AS THEY CAME.

- 6 -18 - 39

VAL WONDERS HOW LONG THE LAVISH BANQUETS CAN LAST, FOR THE HUNS' RESOURCES ARE UNLIMITED.

"WOULD IT NOT BE WELL TO CONSERVE OUR SUPPLIES, CAMORAN?" "SIR VALIANT, NO ENEMY WILL EVER ALTER THE WAYS OF LIVING AT ANDELKRAG. WE WILL LIVE, LOVE, FIGHT AND DIE LIKE GENTLEMEN!"
NEXT WEEK-
"THE LAST BANQUET"

Synopsis: THOUGH ASSAILED FURIOUSLY BY ATTILA'S UNTOLD THOUSANDS, ANDELKRAG STILL STANDS UNCONQUERED. THE SCARRED WARRIORS ON THE BATTLEMENTS ARE FEWER NOW, BUT UNDAUNTED, AS THE WEEKS DRAG INTO MONTHS.

IN THE LULL BETWEEN ATTACKS CONTESTS ARE HELD AT THE EXPENSE OF THE HUNS.

WITHIN THE FORTRESS LIFE GOES ON GAILY AS EVER.

BUT UPON THE CRUMBLING WALLS IS ETERNAL VIGILANCE.

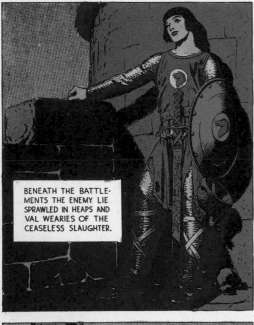

BENEATH THE BATTLEMENTS THE ENEMY LIE SPRAWLED IN HEAPS AND VAL WEARIES OF THE CEASELESS SLAUGHTER.

THAT DREADED DAY AT LAST ARRIVES - OF FOOD AND DRINK THERE IS NO MORE!

6-25-39

THEN CAMORAN ARISES SMILING, "THE BARBARIANS RULE FROM SEA TO SEA - WE ARE THE LAST OF THE WARRIOR - TROUBADORS, BECAUSE OF US THE WORLD HAS BEEN A BETTER PLACE TO LIVE IN, BUT NOW OUR FOOD IS GONE SO TO-MORROW WE WILL DO THAT WHICH WE HAVE TO DO."

NEXT WEEK: "THE LAST MARCH"

Hal Foster

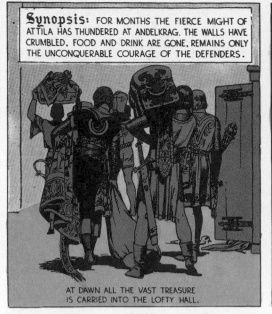

Synopsis: FOR MONTHS THE FIERCE MIGHT OF ATTILA HAS THUNDERED AT ANDELKRAG. THE WALLS HAVE CRUMBLED, FOOD AND DRINK ARE GONE, REMAINS ONLY THE UNCONQUERABLE COURAGE OF THE DEFENDERS.

AT DAWN ALL THE VAST TREASURE IS CARRIED INTO THE LOFTY HALL.

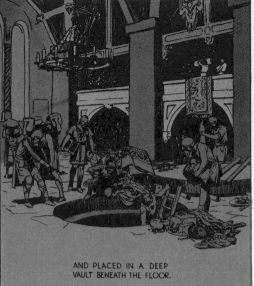

AND PLACED IN A DEEP VAULT BENEATH THE FLOOR.

AND ONE BY ONE THE GRACEFUL, HIGH-SPIRITED LADIES MOUNT SLOWLY THE TOWER STAIRWAY.

CAMORAN, HIMSELF, APPLIES THE TORCH THAT WILL BRING ROOF AND WALLS CRASHING DOWN.

"THE LADIES, CAMORAN, THEY NEVER DESCENDED FROM THE TOWER." AND THE FACE OF CAMORAN IS TERRIBLE TO SEE AS HE ANSWERS —

"THE LADIES DO NOT CHOOSE TO FALL INTO THE HANDS OF THOSE WHO WAIT OUTSIDE."

VAL LOOKS THROUGH THE LOOP-HOLE INTO THE FACES OF THE WILD HUNS AND UNDERSTANDS.

7-2-39

Copr. 1939, King Features Syndicate, Inc.
World rights reserved

HAL FOSTER

QUIETLY, CALMLY THE LAST OF THE WARRIOR-TROUBADOURS GO TO MEET THEIR FOE AND FEARFUL IS THE GLEAM OF THEIR EYES.

NEXT WEEK:
"HOW HEROES DIE"

Synopsis: BEHIND THE BATTERED WALLS OF THE UNCONQUERABLE ANDELKRAG, THE GALLANT DEFENDERS FACE FAMINE. THEY CHOOSE TO MEET DEATH AS WARRIORS FIGHTING THE ENEMY RATHER THAN STARVE MISERABLY. THE FORTRESS IS SET ABLAZE.

DOWN A SECRET PASSAGE BENEATH THE MOAT CAMORAN LEADS THE REMNANT OF THE WARRIOR-TROUBADOURS.

THE TUNNEL'S END IS BLOCKED BY A GREAT ROCK, BUT THEY HURL THEIR WEIGHT AGAINST IT AND IT YIELDS.

OUT INTO THE AFTERNOON SUNLIGHT THEY LEAP, SHOUTING THEIR BATTLE-CRY.

THE BARBARIANS TURN TO MEET THE CHARGING, MAIL-CLAD HURRICANE.

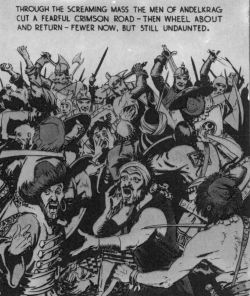

THROUGH THE SCREAMING MASS THE MEN OF ANDELKRAG CUT A FEARFUL CRIMSON ROAD — THEN WHEEL ABOUT AND RETURN — FEWER NOW, BUT STILL UNDAUNTED.

THE SUN GOES DOWN AND STILL A HEROIC FEW FIGHT ON IN THE GATHERING DUSK.

AT LAST ONLY SIR VALIANT STANDS, ALONE WITHIN THE FLAMING CIRCLE OF THE FEARFUL "SINGING SWORD."

Copr. 1939, King Features Syndicate, Inc. World rights reserved   7-9-39

THEN HE, TOO, GOES DOWN BENEATH A STRUGGLING HEAP IN THE DARKNESS.

LONG AND DESPERATELY THEY STRUGGLE, THEN SLOWLY ONE STAGGERS TO HIS FEET, ALONE, ON A FIELD LIT ONLY BY BLAZING ANDELKRAG!

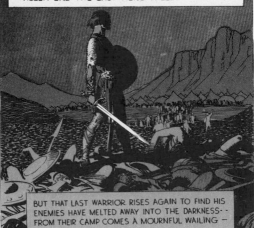

Synopsis: WHEN DEATH APPROACHES THE MEN OF ANDELKRAG MARCH OUT FROM THEIR BURNING FORTRESS AND MEET IT LIKE WARRIORS. NIGHT HAS FALLEN ERE THE LAST HERO FALLS.

BUT THAT LAST WARRIOR RISES AGAIN TO FIND HIS ENEMIES HAVE MELTED AWAY INTO THE DARKNESS-- FROM THEIR CAMP COMES A MOURNFUL WAILING –

"ATTILA IS DEAD, ATTILA IS DEAD," AND THEY GO STREAMING AWAY OVER THE PASS THAT LEADS INTO HUNGARY (WHERE QUARRELS AMONG THE LEADERS FINALLY BREAK THE POWER OF THE HUNS).

A LINE OF CONQUERED FOES LEADS TO THE SPOT WHERE CAMORAN HAD MADE HIS LAST STAND.

VAL TAKES HIS GALLANT CAPTAIN IN HIS ARMS AND STAGGERS TO THE TUNNEL'S MOUTH

UNDER THE MOAT AND WEARILY, STEP BY STEP UP THE EASTERN TOWER

"ALL ANDELKRAG SHALL BE YOUR BIER," AND WRAPPED IN A PURPLE BANNER VAL GIVES HIS CHIEFTIAN TO THE FLAMES.

HIGH UP ON THE HILLSIDE AWAY FROM THE HUN-INFESTED PASS, VAL TURNS TO WATCH THE CASTLE WALLS COME CRASHING DOWN.

THEN SLEEPS UNTIL THE NEXT DAY'S NOON...

....WHILE TWO SHREWD, AVARICIOUS EYES PEER HUNGRILY AT THE JEWELS SPARKLING ON THE HILT OF THE "SINGING SWORD."

NEXT WEEK: "SLITH—

Synopsis: ANDELKRAG, THE UNCONQUERABLE, BECOMES A SMOLDERING RUIN AND THE ONE BATTERED SURVIVOR STAGGERS WEARILY INTO THE HILLS. WHEN HE AWAKES THE NOON DAY SUN IS SPARKLING ON THE JEWELED HILT OF HIS "SINGING SWORD."

WHILE ACROSS THE POOL TWO SHREWD EYES ARE PEERING HUNGRILY AT THE FLASHING GEMS WAITING.

VAL STEPS TO THE EDGE OF THE CLEAR SPRING AND REMOVES HIS SWORD AND MAIL.

THE COOL, SPARKLING WATER FEELS SO GOOD ON HIS BRUISED AND WEARY BODY THAT HE FAILS TO NOTICE THE CROUCHING FIGURE CREEPING CLOSER.

UNTIL A DISLODGED PEBBLE COMES RATTLING DOWN AND SPLASHES BESIDE HIM.

THEN COMES ACTION SO QUICK THAT HIS ATTACKER NEVER KNEW WHAT HAD HAPPENED UNTIL·······

·····HE FINDS HIMSELF HELPLESS. VAL IS CALMLY DROWNING HIM WHEN CURIOSITY GETS THE BETTER OF HIM AND THE VICTIM IS HAULED OUT ON THE BANK.

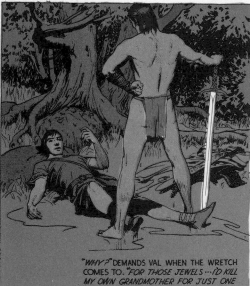

"WHY?" DEMANDS VAL WHEN THE WRETCH COMES TO. "FOR THOSE JEWELS···I'D KILL MY OWN GRANDMOTHER FOR JUST ONE OF THE GEMS IN THAT FINE SWORD KILT."

7-23-39

"FOR I AM SLITH, THIEF AND ROBBER, JUGGLER, ACTOR, SINGER AND MAGICIAN. I LIVE BY MY WITS AND EVERY MAN IS MY ENEMY. I AM REALLY NOT WORTH KILLING··· I HOPE," AND GRINS DISARMINGLY.

HAL FOSTER

VAL LAUGHS AT HIS IMPUDENCE AND KICKS HIM TO HIS FEET-WHEREUPON THE GRATEFUL RASCAL LEADS THE WAY TO HIS NEARBY CAMP AND A WELCOME SUPPER.

NEXT WEEK: **"BAD COMPANY"**

"WON THEM WITH CROOKED DICE", SLITH EXPLAINS, "FROM A NOBLEMAN WHO OVERTAXED HIS SERFS ····· ONE OF US WAS A VILLAIN."

"I WAS STOLEN WHEN A CHILD, SOLD INTO SLAVERY. I'VE BEEN BEATEN, ROBBED AND HUNTED LIKE A WILD BEAST — I AM WHAT MEN HAVE MADE ME."

"SO I EARN MY BREAD BY TRICKS AND TRICKERY. I ENTERTAIN FOR FOOD, GAMBLE FOR PLEASURE AND CHEAT FOR PROFIT."

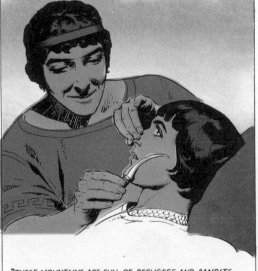

"THESE MOUNTAINS ARE FULL OF REFUGEES AND BANDITS — HOLD STILL! ··· AND ON THE PLAINS ARE BANDS OF HUNS."

"WE NEED FOOD SO WE WILL FIND A CAMP AND I'LL SHOW YOU HOW I GET A LIVING."

"LOOK! A BAND OF HUNS APPROACHES — YOU HIDE AND I'LL TRICK THE STUPIDS INTO FEEDING US."

HIDDEN AMONG THE ROCKS, VAL WATCHES SLITH DELUDING THE HATED HUNS.

7-30-39

OH! HOW HE HATES THE HUNS! ···· THE HUNS WHO HAD DESTROYED GLORIOUS ANDELKRAG AND ALL ITS SPLENDID PEOPLE ····· HE STANDS UP, SCOWLING.

THE SUN, FLASHING ON THE JEWELED SWORD HILT CATCHES THE HUNS' EYES.

NEXT WEEK:
AGAIN THE SWORD SINGS"

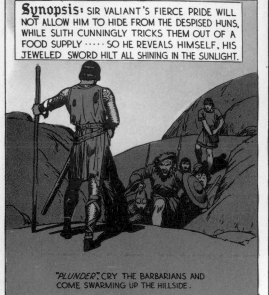

SIR VALIANT'S FIERCE PRIDE WILL NOT ALLOW HIM TO HIDE FROM THE DESPISED HUNS, WHILE SLITH CUNNINGLY TRICKS THEM OUT OF A FOOD SUPPLY ..... SO HE REVEALS HIMSELF, HIS JEWELED SWORD HILT ALL SHINING IN THE SUNLIGHT.

"PLUNDER", CRY THE BARBARIANS AND COME SWARMING UP THE HILLSIDE.

SLITH FITS A MISSILE IN HIS SLING AND IS ABOUT TO CRACK A SKULL OR TWO, WHEN HIS ATTENTION IS ARRESTED·····

...ARRESTED BY VAL'S QUIET, CONFIDENT MANNER, AS WITH NEITHER SHIELD NOR HELMET HE AWAITS THE ONSLAUGHT OF THE CLIMBING HUNS. SLITH SEEKS A VANTAGE POINT, TO WATCH, HIS SLING READY.

BUT HE FORGETS TO USE IT ·····HE IS LOST IN ADMIRATION FOR THE PRETTIEST PIECE OF SWORD PLAY HE HAS EVER SEEN.

FOR VAL SEEMS TO KNOW EVERY MOVE HIS ENEMIES ARE ABOUT TO MAKE AND HIS NIMBLE SWORD FLASHES OUT UNEXPECTEDLY.

WITH HIS STAFF HE SMOTHERS THEIR ATTACK, MANEUVERING SO THEY ARE ALWAYS IN EACH OTHER'S WAY.

WHEN THE LAST HUN SUDDENLY REMEMBERS HEALTHIER PLACES FAR AWAY SLITH IS APPLAUDING JOYOUSLY.

"I KNOW YOUR SECRET," HE CRIES, "CO-ORDINATION! SO QUICK IS YOUR EYE YOU SEE THINGS PRACTICALLY IN SLOW MOTION ···THE CHARM OF THE 'SINGING SWORD' HAS NOTHING TO DO WITH IT."

"LISTEN, WORM!, THE SINGING SWORD BEARS A CHARM FOR HIM WHO USES IT IN A GOOD CAUSE. I PREFER TO BELIEVE THAT!"

NEXT WEEK: "SETTING A TRAP"

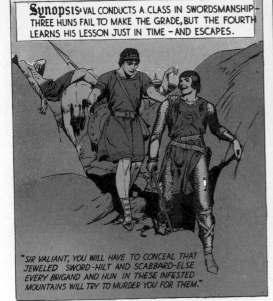

Synopsis: VAL CONDUCTS A CLASS IN SWORDSMANSHIP—THREE HUNS FAIL TO MAKE THE GRADE, BUT THE FOURTH LEARNS HIS LESSON JUST IN TIME—AND ESCAPES.

"SIR VALIANT, YOU WILL HAVE TO CONCEAL THAT JEWELED SWORD-HILT AND SCABBARD—ELSE EVERY BRIGAND AND HUN IN THESE INFESTED MOUNTAINS WILL TRY TO MURDER YOU FOR THEM."

"INCLUDING YOURSELF, SLITH, MY NIMBLE FRIEND ······ WELL, LET'S SEE WHAT THE LATE HUNS HAVE LEFT US IN THE WAY OF FOOD AND CLOTHING."

SEEING THE VALUE OF SLITH'S ADVICE, VAL MAKES A COVER FOR THE JEWELED SCABBARD AND PUTS A BINDING OVER THE BRIGHT HILT.

"NOW THIS COSTUME MAY SUIT YOU, BUT NOT ME, I NOT ONLY LOOK LIKE A HUN, BUT, BY ZEUS, I SMELL LIKE ONE!"

FOLLOWED BY THE PROTESTING SLITH, VAL GOES IN SEARCH OF A COSTUME FITTING HIS RANK ··· AND HIS VANITY!

HIGH ABOVE THE PASS WHEREBY THE PLUNDERING HUNS RETURN INTO PANNONIA THE TWO LADS WATCH FOR VAL'S NEW SUIT TO COME ALONG.

JUST AT SUNDOWN VAL EXCLAIMS:— "LOOK ··· LEADING THAT TROOP IS MY NEW OUTFIT WITH AN UNFORTUNATE HUN CHIEFTAIN IN IT!"

8-13-39

WHILE THE HUNS ARE CAMPING FOR THE NIGHT, VAL PREPARES A TRICK THAT WILL SEPARATE THE UNLUCKY LEADER FROM HIS FOLLOWERS.

AT DAWN THEY ARE IN THEIR PLACE PREPARED TO TAKE A SUIT OF CLOTHING AWAY FROM A TROOP OF FIFTY ARMED HUNS.

NEXT WEEK "SLITH ABANDONED"

Synopsis: VAL FINDS HIS BATTERED NORTHERN ARMOR UNSUITED TO SOUTHERN EUROPE. HE GOES SHOPPING FOR A NEW OUTFIT AND, WHEN HE SEES IT, FINDS HE HAS TO REMOVE THE HUN INSIDE. AT A STEEP POINT ON THE TRAIL VAL PREPARES A TRAP TO SEPARATE HIS VICTIM FROM THE FOLLOWING TROOP OF RAIDERS.

AS THE HUN CAPTAIN PASSES THEIR HIDING-PLACE, VAL FORCES OUT THE TRIGGER AND THE GREAT PINE COMES CRASHING DOWN···

····THERE IS A GREAT CONFUSION AS THE TERRIFIED HORSES REAR AND PLUNGE·· VAL SPRINGS FORWARD···

··· BUT HIS CHOSEN VICTIM IS BEING CARRIED DOWN THE TRAIL ON HIS TERROR-STRICKEN MOUNT··· ·VAL LEAPS UPON THE SECOND HUN.

A SHORT, DEADLY STRUGGLE AND VAL IS CLATTERING RECKLESSLY DOWN THE STEEP, ROCKY PATH IN PURSUIT

CLOSE ON THE HUN'S LEFT FLANK RIDES VAL FORCING HIS ENEMY TO TURN IN THE SADDLE AND FIGHT AWKWARDLY··· SOONER OR LATER HE MUST GET OFF BALANCE.

IT HAPPENS, AND AS THE HUN GRASPS FOR HIS SADDLE, VAL CLOSES IN, HOOKS A TOE UNDER HIS ADVERSARY'S FOOT AND TUMBLES HIM OFF.

"I SHOULD KILL YOU," SAYS VAL,"BUT I DON'T WANT TO SPOIL MY NEW CLOTHES ····· TAKE THEM OFF !"

8-20-39

MEANWHILE, POOR SLITH IS HAVING TROUBLE - THE FALLEN TREE IS A BARRIER TO THE HORSES, BUT THE MEN HAVE DISMOUNTED AND COME SWARMING OVER IN PURSUIT

HEARING A NOISE VAL LOOKS UP AND THERE, COMING ROUND THE MOUNTAIN, IS SLITH FOLLOWED BY THE EVER-FAITHFUL SOCRATES AND FIFTY SHOUTING BARBARIANS!

NEXT WEEK: *"HOW THE RACE ENDED"*

Synopsis: VAL TOPPLES A GREAT PINE ACROSS THE TRAIL SEPARATING A TROOP OF HUNS FROM THEIR CAPTAIN WHO HAPPENS TO WEAR A SUIT OF CLOTHES VAL WANTS. VAL GETS HIS OUTFIT, BUT ALL SLITH GETS IS SOME EXERCISE, AS FIFTY HUNS ON FOOT PURSUE HIM OVER THE MOUNTAIN.

AT VAL'S CALL SLITH COMES SPRINTING DOWN THE HILLSIDE.

"YOU ARE GOING THE WRONG WAY, VAL!"
"NO, I AM NOT. FOLLOW ME!"

THE HUNS LEAVE BEHIND TWO OF THEIR NUMBER TO CLEAR THE TRAIL—A TASK THEY NEVER COMPLETE......

...FOR VAL AND SLITH LEAP THE BARRIER, CUT THEM DOWN....

...AND STAMPEDE THEIR MOUNTS AND BAGGAGE ANIMALS UP THE PATH.

LEAVING THE TRAIL THEY CROSS THE VALLEY FLOOR AND DRIVE THEIR PLUNDER UP A SIDE CANYON.

AT THE NARROW PART THEY FELL TREES TO KEEP THE CAPTURED HORSES FROM ESCAPING.

8-27-39

AND THEN EXAMINE THEIR HAUL.... WEALTH THERE IS IN PLENTY AND ARMS FOR A SMALL ARMY. VAL BECOMES THOUGHTFUL.

HAL FOSTER

"FOR NEARLY SIX YEARS THE HUN HAS ROBBED AND PILLAGED EUROPE..... IT IS TIME NOW THAT SOME ONE ROBS THE HUN..... I WONDER ?"

NEXT WEEK!
"THE LEGION OF HUN-HUNTERS"

Synopsis: BY A GREAT STROKE OF LUCK AND DARING VAL AND SLITH STEAL THE HORSES AND PLUNDER OF A TROOP OF HUN RAIDERS. THERE ARE ARMS AND SUPPLIES FOR A REGIMENT AMONG THE LOOT. ALL VAL NEEDS IS THE REGIMENT TO FULFIL A DARING PLAN.

"SLITH, I NEED SOME FIGHTING MEN, REFUGEES OR BANDITS, SO LONG AS THEY HATE THE HUN. FIND THEM FOR ME."

HIGH UP IN THE HIDDEN VALLEYS THEY FIND SMALL FIELDS AND GARDENS, BUT NOWHERE A SIGN OF HABITATION.

"THEIR HOMES ARE HIDDEN FROM THE HUNS," SAYS SLITH, WHO TAKES A HORN FROM SOCRATES' PACK AND BLOWS A SHEPHERD'S CALL.

THEY ARE ANSWERED FROM A CAUTIOUS DISTANCE. "BRING ME TEN BRAVE FIGHTING MEN AND I WILL GIVE THEM ALL THE FOOD AND LOOT THEY CAN CARRY," CRIES VAL.

AN HOUR LATER SEVERAL STALWART MEN APPEAR. VAL SAYS:- "THE HUNS ROBBED YOU ... I ROB THE HUNS. THE PLUNDER IS YOURS IF YOU CARE TO COME AND TAKE IT."

BACK TO THEIR HIDING-PLACE THEY GO AND EACH OF THE REFUGEES IS ALLOWED TO TAKE ALL HE CAN CARRY ON HIS BACK. SLITH YELPS IN PROTEST AT SUCH USELESS EXTRAVAGANCE.

"NO MAN IS EVER SATISFIED, SLITH EVERY ONE WILL BE BACK AND MORE WILL COME AS THE NEWS IS SPREAD."

9-3-39

AND RIGHT HE IS — SOON A CROWD OF WILD, HALF-STARVED MEN IS CLAMORING FOR FOOD. "I GO TO ROB THE HUN AGAIN TO-NIGHT. WHO WILL FOLLOW ME?"

OH! THE JOY THAT FILLS A WARRIOR'S HEART WHEN ONCE AGAIN HE LEADS FIGHTING MEN TO MEET A FOE!

NEXT WEEK—
THE HUN-HUNTERS

Synopsis: FOR YEARS THE FEROCIOUS HUNS HAVE PILLAGED EUROPE UNHINDERED, BUT NOW THEY IN TURN ARE TO BE PILLAGED. FOR PRINCE VALIANT HAS RECRUITED A SMALL BAND OF REFUGEES AND BANDITS UNITED IN A COMMON HATRED OF THE HUN, AND HAS PLANNED A DARING RAID.

WHERE THE SIDE CANYON ENTERS THE WIDE VALLEY OF THE PASS VAL HALTS HIS LITTLE TROOP.

BELOW THEIR SENTINELS IS A WELL-WATERED MEADOW WHERE THOSE WHO CROSS THE PASS REST AT NIGHTFALL, WEARY FROM A HARD DAY'S TRAVEL.

DOWN FROM THE SNOWY HEIGHTS THAT EVENING COMES A CARAVAN LOADED WITH THE LOOT OF MONTHS OF RAIDING.

WEARILY THEY PITCH THEIR TENTS AND FLING THEMSELVES DOWN TO REST, UNAWARE THAT A GRIM-FACED TROOP IS QUIETLY APPROACHING.

SUDDENLY THERE IS A DRUMMING OF HOOFS - A WILD YELL AND VAL'S HUN-HUNTERS SPREAD PANIC AMONG THE BEWILDERED BARBARIANS.

ERE THE SCATTERED HUNS CAN OR-GANIZE FOR DEFENSE THE BAGGAGE ANIMALS ARE LOADED - TENTS FIRED AND - THE CLATTERING HOOFS FADE AWAY INTO THE DARKNESS.

DAWN FINDS THE RAIDERS, WILD WITH THE JOY OF SUCCESS, DRIVING THEIR RICH PLUNDER INTO THE SIDE VALLEY.

BUT THE HAPPIEST OF ALL IS A CERTAIN YOUNG PRINCE, AS HE ACKNOWLEDGES THE CHEERS OF HIS VICTORIOUS MEN.

NEXT WEEK 'THE HUN-HUNTERS CONTINUED'

FOR YEARS THESE MEN HAVE BEEN HUNTED REFUGEES FROM HUNNISH BRUTALITY; NOW THEY ARE CONQUERORS, WELL-FED AND SLEEPING IN TENTS. THE TIDE AT LAST IS CHANGING.

IN THE MORNING VAL DISMISSES HIS MEN – EACH TO TAKE AS MUCH OF THE PLUNDER AS HE CAN CARRY. HE IS NO FOOL, HE KNOWS THE NEWS OF HIS SUCCESS AND GENEROSITY WILL SPREAD LIKE WILD-FIRE THROUGH THE HILLS

THE RESPONSE IS ENTHUSIASTIC – THE MEN OF THE HILLS HAVE AT LAST FOUND A LEADER WHO PROMISES THEM FOOD, FIGHTING AND REVENGE···A FINE TROOP GATHERS.

FIRST VAL SENDS OUT SPIES TO GATHER NEWS AND LEARNS THAT SMALL BANDS OF HUNS ARE NO LONGER USING THE PASS, BUT ARE GATHERING IN LARGE NUMBERS BEFORE CROSSING.

WITH SOCRATES CARRYING A WEEK'S PROVISIONS VAL AND SLITH MAKE A CAREFUL STUDY OF THE PASS AND THE SURROUNDING COUNTRY·····

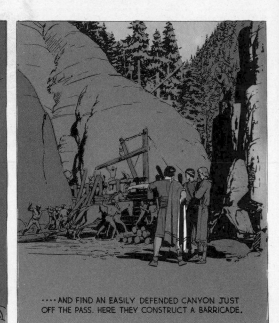

·····AND FIND AN EASILY DEFENDED CANYON JUST OFF THE PASS. HERE THEY CONSTRUCT A BARRICADE.

SLITH CLEVERLY BUILDS A MODEL OF THE BATTLE GROUND AND VAL REHEARSES HIS CAREFULLY CHOSEN LEADERS IN HIS PLAN.

9-17-39

HAL FOSTER

AT LAST COMES WORD THAT THE HUNS ARE ON THE MARCH, A THOUSAND FIGHTING MEN LEADING, THEN THE BAGGAGE TRAIN FOLLOWED BY FIVE HUNDRED MORE WARRIORS. THE DAY HAS AT LAST ARRIVED. VAL CALLS HIS THREE HUNDRED INTO ACTION!

NEXT WEEK:
"AT THE BARRICADE"

Synopsis: PRINCE VALIANT'S BAND OF HUN HUNTERS HAVE MADE THE PASS SO DANGEROUS THAT THE HUNS NO LONGER DARE CROSS IT UNTIL THEY HAVE GATHERED A CONSIDERABLE FORCE TO GUARD THEIR RICH PLUNDER.

HIDDEN IN THEIR NARROW GORGE VAL'S HARDY TROOP AWAIT THE SIGNAL THAT WILL WARN THEM OF THE HUN'S APPROACH.

UP THE WINDING VALLEY COMES THE HUN CARAVAN-GUARDED BY A THOUSAND WARRIORS IN FRONT AND FIVE HUNDRED IN THE REAR.

JUST AS THE BAGGAGE TRAIN REACHES THE MOUTH OF VAL'S GORGE A DISTANT HORN SOUNDS AND ACROSS THE WIDE VALLEY SWEEPS A TROOP OF HORSEMEN....

.....STRAIGHT FOR THE HUNS THEY GALLOP, THEN, SEEING THE STRENGTH OF THEIR VICTIMS, TURN AND FLEE. WITH A WILD SHOUT THE VANGUARD SETS OFF IN PURSUIT.

WITH THE VANGUARD DECOYED FAR OUT ACROSS THE VALLEY AND THE REARGUARD STRUNG OUT BEHIND ON A NARROW TRAIL VAL AND HIS MEN SUDDENLY APPEAR AND TAKE CHARGE OF THE BAGGAGE TRAIN.......

......DRIVING IT OFF THE TRAIL UP THE GORGE AND PAST THEIR BARRICADE, WHICH IS AT ONCE CLOSED.

MEANWHILE THE PATH IN FRONT OF THE REARGUARD IS BLOCKED WITH DEBRIS—

9-24-39

FAR ACROSS THE VALLEY THE HUN VANGUARD DISCOVERS THEY ARE CHASING ONLY MOUNTED BOYS AND OLD MEN-AND-TOO LATE, REALIZE THEY HAVE BEEN TRICKED.

WILD WITH RAGE AT THE HOAX PUT UPON THEM THEY GALLOP BACK ONLY TO FIND THEIR PLUNDER DRIVEN UP THE GORGE AND THE WAY BLOCKED BY A BARRICADE!

NEXT WEEK "THE VANISHED CARAVAN"

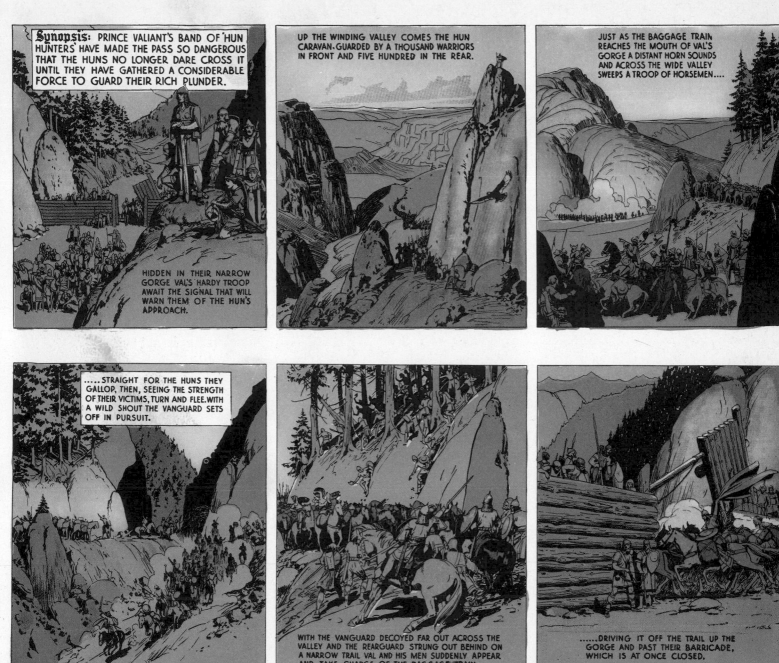

Synopsis: PRINCE VALIANT'S PLAN WORKS PERFECTLY; THE HUNS ARE TRICKED INTO LEAVING THEIR BAGGAGE TRAIN UNGUARDED AND THE BAND OF "HUN-HUNTERS" SWOOP DOWN AND DRIVE IT UP THEIR FORTIFIED GORGE.

UNABLE TO STORM THE BARRICADE THE HUN CHIEFTAIN ORDERS HIS MEN TO DISMOUNT AND CLIMB AROUND IT.

BUT VAL IS READY – SOON THE BARRICADE IS A RAGING MASS OF FLAME, AND HIS MEN RETREATING.

THOUGH A DEMON WARRIOR ON HORSEBACK, THE HUN IS A POOR FIGHTER ON FOOT AND IT WILL BE HOURS BEFORE THEY CAN GET THEIR HORSES PAST THE BURNING BARRIER.

MEANWHILE, THE CARAVAN HAS BEEN DIVIDED AND SENT OUT OF THE VALLEY BY A DOZEN DIFFERENT PATHS.

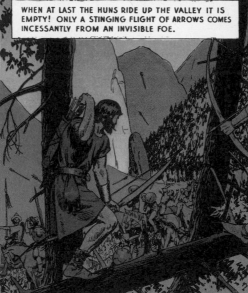

WHEN AT LAST THE HUNS RIDE UP THE VALLEY IT IS EMPTY! ONLY A STINGING FLIGHT OF ARROWS COMES INCESSANTLY FROM AN INVISIBLE FOE.

RIGHT UP TO THE HEAD OF THE VALLEY GO THE HUNS WITH NEVER A SIGN OF THEIR FABULOUSLY RICH CARAVAN. IN RAGE AND DESPAIR THEY RETURN.

AND THEIR RETREAT GIVES VAL ANOTHER SURPRISING VICTORY, BUT HE REMAINS CALM – THE HUN WILL SEEK REVENGE!

10-1-38

FOR THREE DAYS VAL KEEPS HIS MEN IN HAND UNTIL THE LAST OF THE NOW STARVING HUNS HAS CROSSED THE PASS....THEN THEY HOLD A VICTORY FEAST.

IN FAR OFF PANNONIA THE NEWS OF VAL'S RAIDS CAUSES GREAT ANGER. *"THE HUN MUST BE FEARED AND RESPECTED!"* CRIES THE GREAT KHAN AND CALLS UP AN ARMY.

NEXT WEEK: **TROUBLE!**

The Grand Victory

Synopsis: UNDER PRINCE VALIANT'S DARING LEADERSHIP THE "LEGION OF HUN-HUNTERS" HAS STRUCK AGAIN AND AGAIN AS THE HUNS CROSS THE PASS; RUNNING OFF THEIR HORSES, THEIR PLUNDER AND THEIR SUPPLIES. WITH NEVER A CHANCE TO STRIKE BACK AT THEIR NIMBLE FOE, THE HUNS ARE LEFT TO STARVE IN A WILDERNESS OF THEIR OWN MAKING.

THE RAGE OF KALLA KHAN IS TERRIBLE AS THE FAMISHED SURVIVORS STRAGGLE BACK INTO PANNONIA WITH TIDINGS OF STILL MORE DEFEATS.

THE KHAN SUMMONS "KARNAK, THE FEROCIOUS." AND SAYS; "TAKE AN ARMY, CLEAR THE PASS AND FORTIFY IT. TWO MOONS FROM TO-DAY RETURN WITH THE HEAD OF PRINCE VALIANT!"

"YONDER ARE TWO STAKES.... ON ONE IS THE HEAD OF A DEFEATED GENERAL. THE OTHER IS FOR THE HEAD OF PRINCE VALIANT..... OR YOUR OWN!"

ON THE PLAIN BELOW THE PASS THE VAST HUN ARMY STARTS BUILDING A FORTIFIED CAMP.

BUT NEWS OF VAL'S ASTOUNDING SUCCESS HAS SPREAD FAR AND WIDE AND HIS ARMY GROWS. EVEN SLY VALENTINIAN SENDS 500 ARMED AND MOUNTED KNIGHTS FROM ROME......

......AND FROM SPAIN THE KING SENDS A THOUSAND HARD-FIGHTING VISIGOTHS WITH ARMS AND MONEY.

BUT, BEST OF ALL, FROM KING ARTHUR'S COURT IN FAR-OFF BRITAIN, COME TWO BATTERED KNIGHTS ERRANT.... MIGHTY TRISTRAM AND MERRY SIR GAWAIN!

10-8-39

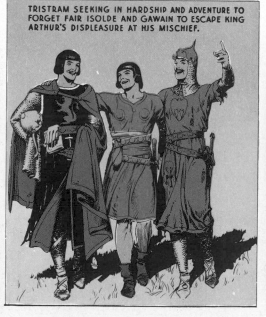

TRISTRAM SEEKING IN HARDSHIP AND ADVENTURE TO FORGET FAIR ISOLDE AND GAWAIN TO ESCAPE KING ARTHUR'S DISPLEASURE AT HIS MISCHIEF.

THE RECKLESS, CAREFREE DAYS ARE OVER NOW, FOR VAL FINDS HIMSELF THE RESPONSIBLE CHIEFTAIN OF A CONSIDERABLE ARMY WITH THE MIGHT OF THE HUN NATION PITTED AGAINST HIM!

NEXT WEEK— **TREACHERY!**

Synopsis: THE RAPIDLY GROWING FORCES UNDER PRINCE VALIANT'S LEADERSHIP HOLD THE PASS, BUT IN THE PLAIN BELOW THE HUNS' VAST ARMY HAS BUILT A STRONGLY FORTIFIED BASE AND MORE MEN AND SUPPLIES ARRIVE DAILY.

HUN SCOUTS TRY DESPERATELY TO FIND OUT THE STRENGTH OF THE "HUN-HUNTERS."

IN THE EXCITEMENT OF THESE SKIRMISHES VAL FORGETS HIS CARES, AND ONCE AGAIN GOES CRASHING INTO THE FRAY, SIDE BY SIDE WITH TRISTRAM AND GAWAIN!

BUT SPIES ARE BEING FOUND IN GREAT NUMBERS, COMING UP BEHIND THEM FROM THE FAR SIDE OF THE PASS – FROM A CAPTURED OFFICER VAL LEARNS THE CAUSE.....

...TWO DAYS' RIDE TO THE SOUTH IS A PASS GUARDED BY THE BEAUTIFUL WALLED CITY OF PANDARIS. DUKE CESARIO HELD THE PASS AGAINST THE HUN, BUT HIS COUSIN, PISCARO, AIDED BY TREACHERY AND THE HUNS, IMPRISONS CESARIO, SETS HIMSELF UP AS TYRANT AND OPENS THE PASS TO THE BARBARIANS.

LOOKING DOWN UPON THEIR ENEMY'S PREPARATIONS, THEY ESTIMATE THAT IT WILL BE TWO MOONS BEFORE THEY ARE READY TO ATTACK. WITH THE ODDS ALREADY 20 TO 1 AGAINST THEM, THE "HUN-HUNTERS'" POSITION WILL BE HOPELESS IF THEY ARE ATTACKED FROM THE REAR ALSO.

DESPITE THE OBJECTIONS OF HIS COUNCIL, VAL SETS OUT FOR PANDARIS WITH A FORCE CONSISTING ONLY OF NIMBLE SLITH AND LONG-EARED SOCRATES!

NEXT WEEK—
PANDARIS!

HAL FOSTER

10-15-39

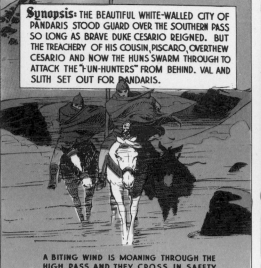

A BITING WIND IS MOANING THROUGH THE HIGH PASS AND THEY CROSS IN SAFETY, OBSCURED BY THE SWIRLING SNOW.

IN THE FRIENDLY DARKNESS THEY DRIFT SILENTLY PAST THE SMALL HUN ENCAMPMENTS ON THE FAR SIDE OF THE PASS.

SEVERAL MILES FROM PANDARIS VAL HALTS AT THE HOME OF ONE GUIDO, A FAITHFUL FRIEND OF CESARIO, FOR REST AND INFORMATION.

"PISCARO IS A CRUEL TYRANT, WEAK AND VICIOUS. THE PEOPLE OF PANDARIS WOULD RESTORE BRAVE CESARIO TO POWER, BUT THEIR CITY IS FILLED WITH HUNS AND HE WHO RAISES HIS VOICE AGAINST PISCARO IS SWIFTLY MURDERED."

DRESSED AS PEDDLERS, VAL, SLITH AND SOCRATES APPROACH THE FAIR CITY, ITS SPIRES AND DOMES GLEAMING IN THE SUNLIGHT.

"WHAT IS YOUR BUSINESS WITHIN OUR CITY?" DEMANDS THE OFFICER AT THE GATE. "WE ARE MERCHANTS COME TO CHEAT THE HUNS," ANSWERS VAL BOLDLY. LOOKING CAUTIOUSLY AROUND, THE OFFICER WHISPERS. "PASS, FRIEND!"

WITHIN THE CITY IS THE BROODING SILENCE OF AN UNHAPPY PEOPLE. THE TWO FRIENDS ARE MOVING TOWARD THE PALACE, WHEN TRUMPETS SOUND.....

10-22-39

AND THE BRUTAL SOLDIERS CLEAR A PATH AMONG THE PEOPLE, AS THE DUKE RIDES FORTH!

NEXT WEEK—
VAL'S DEFIANCE!

Synopsis: PRINCE VALIANT AND SLITH TRAVEL TO PANDARIS TO FIND OUT WHY THAT WALLED CITY SHOULD LET THE HUNS PASS TO ATTACK HIS "HUN-HUNTERS" IN THE REAR. HE FINDS THAT TREACHEROUS PISCARO HAS SEIZED THE DUKE CESARIO AND ASSUMED COMMAND OF THE CITY.

"KNEEL IN THE DUST, SONS OF DOGS. HIS HIGHNESS APPROACHES!" CRY THE SOLDIERS, AS THEY CLEAR A PATH WITH THEIR RODS

THE FALSE DUKE RIDES BY, DAINTILY WAVING A PERFUMED TASSEL BEFORE HIS WEAK, VINDICTIVE FACE.

"KNEEL, SIR," WHISPER THE CITIZENS. "IT IS DEATH MOST TERRIBLE TO OFFEND THE DUKE." BUT VAL IS A PRINCE AND KNIGHT OF THE ROUND TABLE AND WILL KNEEL TO NO SUCH TYRANT! "I'VE SEEN BETTER MEN IN MY FATHER'S STABLES!" QUOTH HE.

THE SOMBER EYE OF THE TYRANT FALLS ON THE ERECT FIGURE OF THE PRINCE AND HIS FACE FLUSHES WITH RAGE. "BREAK HIS LEGS THAT HE MAY BE GLAD TO KNEEL," HE COMMANDS.

"THANKS FOR REMINDING ME OF MY LEGS," SHOUTS VAL AND PROMPTLY USES THEM.

HE IS RAPIDLY OUTRUNNING HIS PURSUERS WHEN, BY ILL LUCK, HE DODGES INTO A BLIND STREET FROM WHICH THERE IS NO OUTLET.

THE NOISE OF PURSUIT IS DRAWING DESPERATELY NEAR WHEN SUDDENLY HE IS SEIZED BY A STRONG HAND AND JERKED INTO A DOORWAY.

10-29-39

VAL WHIPS OUT HIS READY DAGGER, BUT A CALM VOICE SAYS: "WILL YOU TRUST YOURSELF TO ME OR TO THE SOLDIERS OUTSIDE?"

NEXT WEEK—
THE "LIBERATORS"

HE DISAPPEARS UPWARD IN THE DARKNESS AND VAL QUICKLY FOLLOWS—HIS GROPING HANDS FIND THE NICHES AND HE MOUNTS RAPIDLY.

THEY EMERGE INTO THE ADJOINING HOUSE. *"THIS IS THE SECRET MEETING-PLACE OF THE 'LIBERATORS.' I TRUST YOUR HATRED OF PISCARO WILL MAKE YOU ONE OF US."*

THE "LIBERATORS" ARE FAITHFUL FRIENDS OF DUKE CESARIO, FORCED BY PISCARO'S WEAK FEROCITY TO SEEK SAFETY IN DISGUISE AND HIDING.... AND IN THEIR HIDING-PLACES THEY PLOT.

VAL LEARNS THAT THE CITIZENS LOATHE THE CRUEL PISCARO, BUT THE MENACING SHADOW OF THE HUN KEEPS THEM COWED. ONLY THROUGH THE DEATH OF PISCARO AND LIBERATION OF DUKE CESARIO CAN VAL EXPECT HELP FOR HIS TROOPS.

ALL THROUGH THE DAY AND INTO THE NIGHT THE SOLDIERS SEARCH FOR PRINCE VALIANT, FOR THEY FEAR THEIR MASTER'S WRATH IF THEY FAIL.

LIKE A GHOST SLITH HAUNTS THE STREETS AND ALLEYS, SEARCHING DAY AND NIGHT FOR HIS FRIEND.

FOR A BRIEF WHILE VAL REMAINS IN HIDING THEN, DONNING THE GARB OF A HUN WARRIOR, HE VENTURES FORTH.

BUT, NO MATTER WHAT CLOTHES HE WEARS, THERE IS ONE THING HE CANNOT DISGUISE; HE IS A KING'S SON AND LOOKS IT EVERY INCH!

11-5-39

HAL FOSTER

HE IS RECOGNIZED IMMEDIATELY, OVER-POWERED AND DRAGGED OFF TO THE PALACE... AND PISCARO'S VENGEANCE!

NEXT WEEK—
PISCARO'S TORTURE ROOM!

A DISGUISE CANNOT HIDE HIS PRINCELY BEARING; VAL IS RECOGNIZED AND QUICKLY CAPTURED.

IN A ROOM DRUGGED WITH THE VAPOR OF PERFUME AND INCENSE VAL STANDS BEFORE PISCARO AND MEETS THE UNBLINKING HATRED IN HIS EYES.

"SO - THEY HAVE BROUGHT YOU TO ME AT LAST! EVERYONE FEARS ME....ONLY YOU DEFY ME....BUT YOU HAVE NOT YET VISITED MY TORTURE CHAMBER. SOON YOU WILL WHIMPER FOR THE RELIEF OF DEATH," AND PISCARO SNICKERS.

VAL IS DRAGGED BRUTALLY DOWN TO A DUNGEON CELL......

...... AND CHAINED TO THE DAMP, COLD WALL.

DEATH AND HORROR LURK IN THE VERY AIR OF THIS GRUESOME PLACE. VAL'S MIND IS BUSY WITH PLANS FOR ESCAPE WHEN HE IS STARTLED BY A VOICE.

THROUGH A SMALL WINDOW BETWEEN THE CELLS PEERS A PALE FACE. *"I AM DUKE CESARIO,"* HE WHISPERS. *"THE SCREAMS OF PISCARO'S VICTIMS ARE DRIVING ME MAD, IS THERE ANY HOPE OF RESCUE?"*

VAL TELLS HIM OF THE "LIBERATORS" WHILE A SPY LISTENS OUTSIDE. FOR THESE WINDOWS BETWEEN THE CELLS ARE FOR THE PURPOSE OF ENCOURAGING TALK.

11-12-39

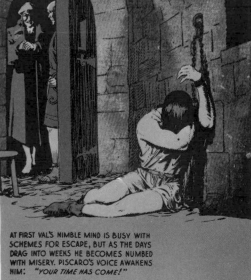

AT FIRST VAL'S NIMBLE MIND IS BUSY WITH SCHEMES FOR ESCAPE, BUT AS THE DAYS DRAG INTO WEEKS HE BECOMES NUMBED WITH MISERY. PISCARO'S VOICE AWAKENS HIM: *"YOUR TIME HAS COME!"*

NEXT WEEK-
THE RACK!

Synopsis: TO PREVENT HIS "LEGION OF HUN-HUNTERS" FROM BEING SURROUNDED VAL FINDS IT NECESSARY TO RESCUE THE DUKE CESARIO FROM THE HANDS OF TREACHEROUS PISCARO. UNFORTUNATELY, PRINCE VALIANT, HIMSELF, FALLS INTO PISCARO'S POWER AND HAS SPENT TWO WEEKS CRUELLY CHAINED IN A FILTHY CELL.

"AND NOW THE TIME HAS COME FOR MY SWEET REVENGE," SAYS PISCARO RUBBING HIS COLD HANDS SOFTLY TOGETHER.

THE TORMENTORS STRETCH VAL'S STRONG YOUNG BODY UPON THE RACK AND DRAW THE CHAINS TIGHT, WHILE PISCARO SNICKERS.

"NOW TELL ME WHO THE 'LIBERATORS ARE.... TELL ME WHO PLOTS AGAINST ME, BEFORE YOUR BONES CRACK. NAME THOSE WHO WOULD FREE CESARIO, OR SLOWLY WILL I TEAR YOUR BEAUTIFUL BODY ASUNDER."

THE MERCILESS TORMENTORS BEAR DOWN ON THEIR LEVERS. THERE COMES A HORRIBLE SNAP. VAL SCREAMS, "I'LL TELL, OH! I'LL TELL!".... HE MOANS AND FAINTS.

"CLUMSY FOOLS!" SHRIEKS PISCARO, "IF YOU HAVE KILLED HIM IT IS THE RACK FOR BOTH OF YOU! REVIVE HIM AND WHEN HE CAN TALK, CALL ME."

LATER, WHEN THEY CALL HIM, HE SAYS, "AFTER I HAVE HIS CONFESSION YOU MAY BEAT HIM TO DEATH."

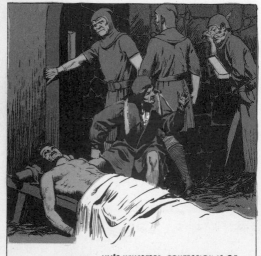

VAL'S WHISPERED CONFESSION IS OF SUCH INTIMATE FAMILY AFFAIRS THAT PISCARO SENDS EVERYONE FROM THE CELL.

BUT VAL REMAINS SILENT SO LONG THAT PISCARO DRAWS HIS DAGGER AND LEANS THREATENINGLY OVER HIS BROKEN AND HELPLESS VICTIM.

11-19-39

HELPLESS? WELL, NOT QUITE... FOR TWO STRONG HANDS SEIZE HIM IN A VICE-LIKE GRIP AND HE IS BORNE SILENTLY TO THE FLOOR.
NEXT WEEK—
A NEW PISCARO.

Synopsis: PRINCE VALIANT'S ARMY NEEDS THE HELP OF CESARIO, DUKE OF PANDARIS, BUT BOTH VAL AND THE DUKE HAVE FALLEN INTO THE POWER OF PISCARO AND, TO GET A CONFESSION, VAL HAS BEEN BROKEN UPON THE RACK.

BUT HIS BROKEN, HELPLESS VICTIM COMES SUDDENLY TO LIFE AND PISCARO IS SEIZED IN A TERRIBLE GRIP.

THE HATRED BORN OF WEEKS OF MISERY GOES INTO THAT ONE SMASHING BLOW

WHEN, FINALLY, PISCARO RETURNS TO CONSCIOUSNESS A GREAT CHANGE HAS TAKEN PLACE—HE HAS HAD A HAIR-CUT, A SHAVE AND A CHANGE OF CLOTHES—HE HAS A BROKEN ARM AND A GREAT FEAR!

"THOUGHT YOU HAD BROKEN ME, DID YOU?" TAUNTS VAL. *"MY BONES DIDN'T BREAK—I JUST CLICKED MY TEETH AND SNAPPED MY FINGERS.....THE REST WAS ACTING!"*

REMOVING THE GAG VAL HITS HIM AGAIN ON THE CHIN TO KEEP HIM QUIET, THEN, IMITATING PISCARO'S MINCING WALK, LEAVES THE DUNGEON.

THROUGH HIS LITTLE WINDOW DUKE CESARIO SEES THE WHOLE ASTONISHING SCENE......EVEN NOW HE CAN HARDLY BELIEVE THAT THE MOANING FIGURE ON THE COT IS NOT VAL.....AND HOPE COMES AGAIN TO THE DUKE.

WITH HEAD DOWN VAL QUICKLY MINCES ACROSS THE BRILLIANT HALL AND TO PISCARO'S ROOMS.

"BRING CESARIO HERE, AND CHAIN HIM TO THE WALL!"

11-26-39

WHEN THEY ARE ALONE, VAL SAYS, *"THE PALACE IS FILLED WITH PISCARO'S FRIENDS. I CANNOT LONG REMAIN UNDETECTED, YET I CANNOT ESCAPE. HAVE YOU A PLAN?"*
NEXT WEEK—
THE PLAN.

Synopsis: VAL TRICKS PISCARO INTO THINKING HIM HELPLESS AND PISCARO ENTERS THE CELL ALONE. VAL LEAVES, DRESSED IN PISCARO'S GARMENTS, WHILE THE PETTY TYRANT STAYS TO FACE THE DOOM HE HAS ORDERED FOR VAL. STILL POSING AS PISCARO, VAL ORDERS THE REAL DUKE BROUGHT FROM THE DUNGEON AND CHAINED TO THE WALL

"THE CASTLE IS FILLED WITH PISCARO'S FRIENDS. NOT ONLY MUST WE ESCAPE, BUT YOU MUST ONCE MORE RULE IN THE CITY OF PANDARIS."

"I HAVE IT!.... WE CANNOT GO TO YOUR FRIENDS, BUT WE CAN BRING YOUR FRIENDS TO US!"

"GET BACK IN YOUR CHAINS, CESARIO, WHILE I SUMMON THE GUARDS, AND REMEMBER... I AM PISCARO AND I HAVE FORCED YOU TO BETRAY YOUR FOLLOWERS."

"MY DEAR COUSIN HAS AT LAST DECIDED TO BETRAY HIS FAITHFUL FRIENDS... TAKE DOWN THEIR NAMES AND ARREST THEM. BY TO-MORROW MY RULE WILL BE UN-QUESTIONED!"

"BUT REMEMBER - ARREST EACH ONE SECRETLY AND LOCK THEM UP UNHARMED, IN THE ARMORY."

AT THE STROKE OF MIDNIGHT THE ORDER IS QUIETLY CARRIED OUT.

INTO THE GLOOMY, ECHOING ARMORY ARE HERDED ALL WHO HAD REMAINED FAITHFUL TO DUKE CESARIO.

HAL FOSTER

Synopsis: STILL POSING AS PISCARO, VAL RESCUES THE REAL DUKE CESARIO FROM THE DUNGEON. EACH MOMENT THEY EXPECT DISCOVERY....VAL ORDERS THE ARREST OF ALL WHO HAVE DARED REMAIN FAITHFUL TO CESARIO AND THEY ARE IMPRISONED IN THE GREAT ARMORY.

"AH! SIR VALIANT, I SEE YOUR PLAN NOW—IN NO OTHER WAY COULD MY FRIENDS ENTER THIS STRONGHOLD."

THEIR PLANNING IS INTERRUPTED BY THE MASTER OF THE DUNGEONS ..."WE HAVE FINISHED WITH PRINCE VALIANT AS YOU DIRECTED, YOUR EXCELLENCY, HE DIED SCREAMING VERY SATISFACTORILY."

"FOOL! I AM PRINCE VALIANT. THAT WAS PISCARO YOU KILLED!"

IN THOSE TWO BLAZING EYES THE MASTER TORTURER READS CLEARLY HIS DOOM—HE LEAPS FOR THE DOOR JUST A SECOND TOO LATE.

"IT IS AN UNPLEASANT FACT THAT YOU AND I SO RESEMBLE THE WORLD'S TWO MEANEST SCOUNDRELS THAT WE CAN ACT THEIR PARTS."

IN AN AGONY OF DESPAIR SLITH WAITS DAY AFTER DAY FOR SOME WORD OF HIS MASTER'S FATE.

AT THE "HUN-HUNTERS" CAMP NO WORD HAS COME FROM THEIR CHIEFTAIN FOR OVER TWO WEEKS. HULTA, THE MESSENGER, QUIETLY SADDLES HIS HORSE AND RIDES FOR PANDARIS.

HE SOON FINDS THE HAGGARD, SLEEPLESS SLITH AND LEARNS FROM HIM OF VAL'S CAPTURE BY PISCARO.

12-10-39

WITH THE SEEMING RECKLESSNESS OF THE BORN HORSEMAN HULTA SPEEDS BACK TO THE CAMP.

NEXT WEEK—
IN THE ARMORY

Synopsis: OVER STEEP MOUNTAIN PATHS RIDES HULTA, BACK TO THE CAMP WHERE THE "HUN-HUNTERS" AWAIT THE ATTACK OF THE HUN ARMY UNDER "KARNAK, THE FEROCIOUS." TO THE CAPTAINS HE REPORTS:--

"PRINCE VALIANT, OUR FEARLESS LEADER, IS HELD PRISONER BY FALSE DUKE PISCARO, HIS FATE UNKNOWN..... IF WE TURN FROM THE HUN ARMY TO ATTACK PISCARO'S WALLED CITY OF PANDARIS WE WILL BE CAUGHT BETWEEN TWO ENEMIES."

ALL AGREE THAT HULTA SPEAKS TRUE..... BUT LATER THEY SPEAK AS FOLLOWS-- SAYS SIR GAWAIN;- "I BELIEVE I SHALL RIDE TO PANDARIS AND HAVE THIS SWORD SHARPENED," AND TRISTRAM REMARKS:- "SPLENDID WEATHER FOR RIDING, I'LL JOIN YOU!"

TO HIS SECOND IN COMMAND VONDERMAN OF THE FOOT-SOLDIERS SAYS:-- "TAKE CHARGE WHILE I LEARN MORE ABOUT HORSEBACK-RIDING!"

CESARIO, THE HORSEMAN REMARKS; "MY WAR-HORSE GROWS STIFF FROM LACK OF EXERCISE, I MUST ATTEND TO IT AT ONCE!"

DE GATIN OF THE ARCHERS SHOUTS; "I GROW WEARY OF THIS WAITING FOR THE HUN ATTACK, I AM OFF FOR A FEW DAYS OF HUNTING!"

BUT YOUNG HULTA, THE MESSENGER, SAYS NOTHING AS USUAL... HE HAS ALREADY LEFT TO JOIN HIS FRIEND, SLITH, IN PANDARIS!

SO IT IS NOT STRANGE THAT THEY ALL MEET ON THE ROAD TO PANDARIS A FEW HOURS LATER!

MEANWHILE, WITHIN THE PALACE, VAL, DISGUISED AS PISCARO AND DUKE CESARIO IN THE GARMENT OF THE LATE CHIEF TORTURER, PREPARE TO PUT THEIR PLAN TO THE TEST.

ORDERING THE ENTIRE PALACE GUARD AS ESCORT, THEY PASS UNDETECTED THROUGH THE CROWDED PALACE INTO THE COURTYARD.

"ARE YOU SURE THE PRISONERS ARE SECURELY CHAINED? HAVE THEY BEEN SEARCHED FOR WEAPONS? THEN GIVE ME THE KEYS THAT I MAY BE SURE."

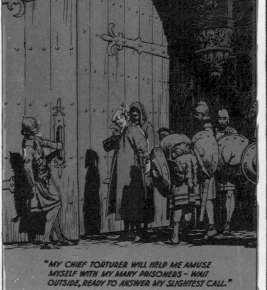

"MY CHIEF TORTURER WILL HELP ME AMUSE MYSELF WITH MY MANY PRISONERS - WAIT OUTSIDE, READY TO ANSWER MY SLIGHTEST CALL."

12-17-39

© 1939, King Features Syndicate, Inc., World rights reserved.

"SPLENDID," GRINS VAL, "ARMS AND ARMOR AND FIFTY OF YOUR GOOD FRIENDS TO USE THEM...TO WORK!"

NEXT WEEK--
HOUSECLEANING.

HAL FOSTER

Synopsis: MASQUERADING AS PISCARO, SIR VALIANT HAS ORDERED THE ARREST OF ALL WHO ARE LOYAL TO THE REAL DUKE CESARIO. VAL AND CESARIO ARE NOW VISITING THEIR PRISONERS, ALONE, IN THE VAST ARMORY.

"CAUTION YOUR FRIENDS TO ABSOLUTE SILENCE AND THEN REVEAL YOURSELF TO THEM, CESARIO."

WHISPERED GREETINGS WITH THEIR NOBLE LEADER OF OLD, THEN HURRIEDLY EACH ONE ARMS HIMSELF..........

"OFFICER, MARCH THE GUARD IN AND FORM AGAINST THE SOUTH WALL."

WITHIN THE DIM BUILDING THEY FIND NOT HELPLESS PRISONERS, BUT FIFTY ARMED KNIGHTS AND THE GRIM-FACED DUKE. *"I WILL JUDGE OF YOUR LOYALTY LATER, UNTIL THEN YOU WILL BE LOCKED IN THIS ARMORY."*

THE FRIENDS AND FOLLOWERS OF SLY PISCARO ARE STARTLED TO SEE HIM LEAD A TROOP OF FULLY ARMED KNIGHTS ACROSS THE GREAT HALL TO THE DUCAL THRONE.

THERE CESARIO REMOVES HIS HELMET— *"I AM CESARIO, RIGHTFUL DUKE OF PANDARIS— THIS IS THE FAR-FAMED PRINCE VALIANT. THESE ARE MY GOOD FRIENDS... WE HAVE COME TO CLEAN HOUSE!"*

DOWN THE DUSTY ROAD INTO PANDARIS COMES TRISTRAM, GAWAIN, HULTA, DE GATIN, VONDERMAN AND CESARIO, THE HORSEMAN, TO RESCUE THEIR LEADER OR SEEK VENGEANCE.

THERE WAS NEVER A MORE UNTIDY HOUSECLEANING!

Hal Foster

NEXT WEEK—
FROM FRYING PAN TO FIRE!

12-24-39

Synopsis: KNOWING ONLY THAT PRINCE VALIANT, THEIR GAY LEADER, IS PRISONER IN PISCARO'S PALACE, HIS FRIENDS STAKE THEIR LIVES ON A DESPERATE RESCUE.

ROUSED FROM HIS WEARY VIGIL BEFORE THE PALACE GATE, FAITHFUL SLITH SEES THEM COMING AND SNATCHES HIS WEAPONS FROM SOCRATES' PACK.

THE MEMORY OF CRUEL INJUSTICES LENDS STRENGTH TO THE ARMS OF DUKE CESARIO'S KNIGHTS, AS THEY SWEEP PISCARO'S FOLLOWERS FROM THE PALACE.

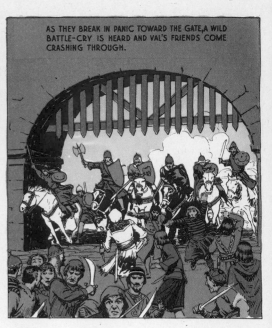

AS THEY BREAK IN PANIC TOWARD THE GATE, A WILD BATTLE-CRY IS HEARD AND VAL'S FRIENDS COME CRASHING THROUGH.

THE MORNING'S WORK IS SMARTLY FINISHED AND WEEKS OF ANXIETY ARE FORGOTTEN, AS GOOD FRIENDS MEET AGAIN. *"THERE IS NOTHING LIKE A LITTLE EXERCISE BEFORE LUNCH TO GIVE ONE AN APPETITE,"* REMARKS TRISTRAM, LOOKING ANXIOUSLY OVER THE SLAIN TO SEE IF ANY OF THE KITCHEN STAFF HAD BEEN WASTED.

"PISCARO IS SLAIN, DUKE CESARIO REIGNS, WE ARE FREE AGAIN!"

THE HUNS HEAR AND TREMBLE - FOR UNDER PISCARO'S RULE THEY DID AS THEY PLEASED AND HEAPED INSULT AND INDIGNITY UPON THE HELPLESS CITIZENS.

THEN COMES A NIGHT OF HORROR, AS THE MEN OF PANDARIS TURN ON THEIR SNEERING OPPRESSORS AND HUNT THEM THROUGH THE STREETS.

12-31-39

NEXT WEEK—
BACK TO DUTY AND A PLAN.

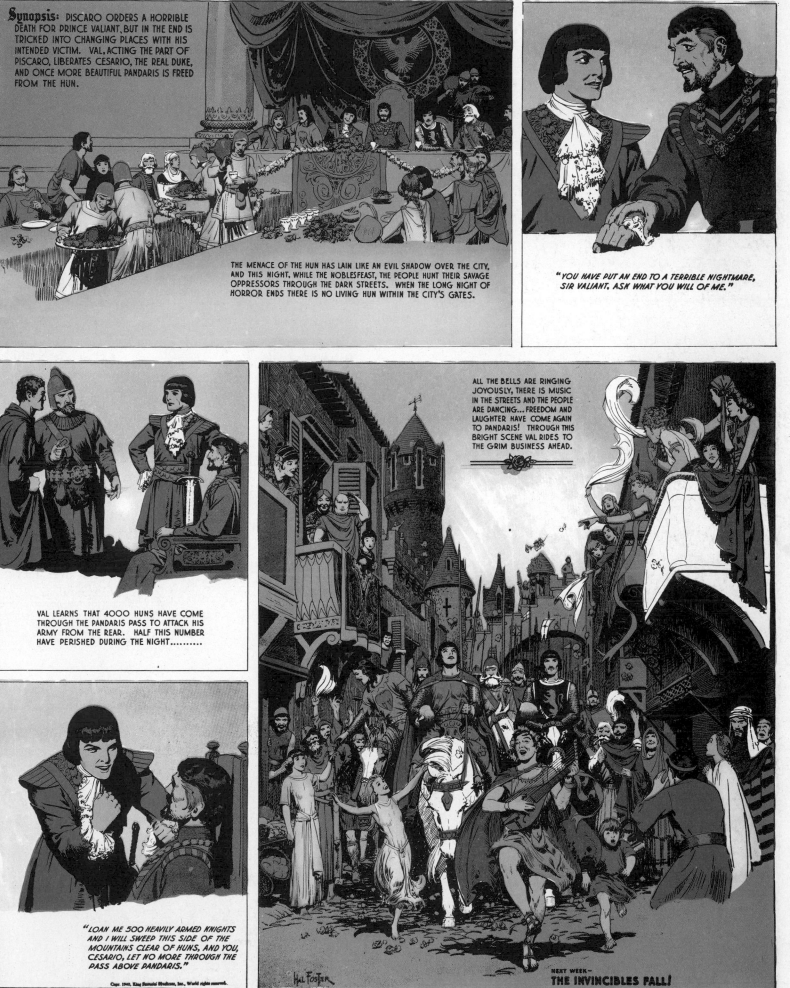

Synopsis: PISCARO ORDERS A HORRIBLE DEATH FOR PRINCE VALIANT, BUT IN THE END IS TRICKED INTO CHANGING PLACES WITH HIS INTENDED VICTIM. VAL, ACTING THE PART OF PISCARO, LIBERATES CESARIO, THE REAL DUKE, AND ONCE MORE BEAUTIFUL PANDARIS IS FREED FROM THE HUN.

THE MENACE OF THE HUN HAS LAIN LIKE AN EVIL SHADOW OVER THE CITY, AND THIS NIGHT, WHILE THE NOBLES FEAST, THE PEOPLE HUNT THEIR SAVAGE OPPRESSORS THROUGH THE DARK STREETS. WHEN THE LONG NIGHT OF HORROR ENDS THERE IS NO LIVING HUN WITHIN THE CITY'S GATES.

"YOU HAVE PUT AN END TO A TERRIBLE NIGHTMARE, SIR VALIANT. ASK WHAT YOU WILL OF ME."

VAL LEARNS THAT 4000 HUNS HAVE COME THROUGH THE PANDARIS PASS TO ATTACK HIS ARMY FROM THE REAR. HALF THIS NUMBER HAVE PERISHED DURING THE NIGHT..........

ALL THE BELLS ARE RINGING JOYOUSLY, THERE IS MUSIC IN THE STREETS AND THE PEOPLE ARE DANCING... FREEDOM AND LAUGHTER HAVE COME AGAIN TO PANDARIS! THROUGH THIS BRIGHT SCENE VAL RIDES TO THE GRIM BUSINESS AHEAD.

"LOAN ME 500 HEAVILY ARMED KNIGHTS AND I WILL SWEEP THIS SIDE OF THE MOUNTAINS CLEAR OF HUNS, AND YOU, CESARIO, LET NO MORE THROUGH THE PASS ABOVE PANDARIS."

HAL FOSTER

NEXT WEEK—
THE INVINCIBLES FALL!

Synopsis: THE GRATEFUL DUKE CESARIO HAS LOANED PRINCE VALIANT 500 KNIGHTS TO DISPERSE THE HUN ARMY THAT MENACES THE REAR OF THE "HUN-HUNTERS." ON THE FAR SIDE OF THE MOUNTAINS VAL'S "LEGION OF HUN-HUNTERS" STILL HOLDS THE PASS IN THE FACE OF THE MAIN HUN ARMY.

TO HIS OFFICERS THE YOUNG PRINCE EXPLAINS HIS PLAN OF ATTACK..... THEY IN TURN FALL BACK AND INSTRUCT THE OTHER KNIGHTS, AS THEY MOVE SWIFTLY FORWARD.

SCOUTS SEE THEM COMING AND SPEED TO THEIR CHIEFTAIN WITH THEIR NEWS.

FOR SIX YEARS THESE BARBARIANS HAVE PILLAGED EUROPE AT WILL WITHOUT DEFEAT --- CONFIDENTLY THEY PREPARE FOR ANOTHER VICTORY.

THE AIR TREMBLES WITH SAVAGE CRIES AND THUNDERING HOOFS, AS THE INVINCIBLE HUN BATTLE FORMATION RUSHES FORWARD,— WINGS WIDE-SPREAD LIKE ENGULFING HORNS.

BUT VAL HAS BEEN SCHOOLED IN BATTLE AT THE COURT OF KING ARTHUR..... AT A COMMAND HIS MAIL-CLAD WARRIORS FORM THE TERRIBLE WEDGE AND CHARGE.

NOTHING HUMAN COULD WITHSTAND THAT IRON-CLAD BLOW. THE HUNS' LEFT WING IS SLICED OFF AND CRUMPLES.

THEN, SWERVING RIGHT AND LEFT THEY SWEEP FURIOUSLY DOWN THE ENEMY LINE.... ROLLING IT BACK IN HELPLESS CONFUSION.

VAL SEEKS AND FINDS THE HUN CHIEFTAIN....SOON THEIR BUSINESS TOGETHER IS FINISHED AND VAL GAZES OVER THE STREWN FIELD. GRIMLY, EFFICIENTLY HIS MEN ARE EXTERMINATING THE FLEEING HUNS.

1-14-40

HIGH ON THE PASS THEIR WORK IS COMPLETED AND THEY PART.... VAL AND HIS FRIENDS TO CROSS OVER AND ONCE AGAIN TAKE COMMAND OF THE "LEGION OF HUN-HUNTERS."

NEXT WEEK—
FAMINE

HAL FOSTER